Low carbon futures

for European households

ECI

ECOFYS

ISR

Tina Fawcett, Kevin Lane, Brenda Boardman

with

Nick Banks, Harriet Griffin, Judith Lipp, Pernille Schiellerup, Riki Therivel

Kornelis Blok, Margreet van Brummelen, Koen Eising, Frank Zegers, Edith Molenbroek

Anibal T. de Almeida, Catarina Nunes, Jorge da Silva Mariano

ACKNOWLEDGEMENTS

While this project represents a collaboration between the three international partner organisations, and was co-ordinated at the Environmental Change Institute, a large debt is owed to many other individuals and institutions. The original inspiration came from Matthew Kestner at DG XVII in Brussels, with his concern for the comparative efficiencies of gas and electricity. This responsibility has now been given to Antonio Paparella in the Energy and Transport Directorate.

The Environmental Change Institute thanks their other colleagues who have contributed to the CADENCE study, in particular Elliot Robertson for the Northern Ireland study, Clio Small for the water heating analysis, Matthew O'Donnell for software development and Richard Pearson for trojan work on the numerical analysis. Sarah Darby and Nathalie Butt provided administrative and editing skills and immeasurable patience, whilst other members of the ECI kept us functioning through their support and guidance.

This project is part-funded by the Market Transformation Programme of the UK's Department of the Environment, Transport and the Regions and the ECI are grateful to Chris Baker at the DETR for his unfailing encouragement and direction and to Fiona Porter of ETSU for her management skills. Other members of the MTP both at ETSU and BRE helped the ECI with discussions on individual appliance groups, under the overall management and guidance of Paul White, at ETSU.

The ECI wish also to thank members of the Energy Saving Trust; Peter Warm and Colin Sutherland for undertaking the household survey of water heaters and their support; Gfk for sales data; Mark Crowther of CRE for a teach-in on water heating. COMET kindly lent us the fridge for the cover and Martin Barfoot is responsible for the cover design artwork. Over a dozen people participated in a workshop, in January 2000, to develop policy and the ECI are grateful to them for their time and enthusiasm.

The Portuguese partners, ISR, wish to thank Comissão de Coordenação da Região Centro, PortGás – Sociedade de Produção e Distribuição de Gás, LusitaniaGás – Companhia de Gás do Centro, S.A., Centro de Conservação de Energia (CCE), Direcção-Geral de Energia (DGE), Eng. Rui Domingos – Portgás, and Eng. Ângela Lobo – DGE.

TABLE OF CONTENTS

Appendices C – T may be found on the Energy and Environment Programme pages on the ECI website: http://www.eci.ox.ac.uk

LIST OF FIGURES

LIST OF TABLES

EXECUTIVE SUMMARY

This report covers domestic gas and electricity energy consumption in lights, appliances and water heating (LAWH) – all residential energy use except space heating and cooling. The detail is for the UK, Netherlands and Portugal to 2020, with a summary for the whole of the European Union.

Domestic energy consumption expected to increase

Of the 210TWh of energy used in LAWH in these three countries, 100TWh is for water heating. The main growth is expected in consumer electronics, where electricity consumption is expected to almost double between 1998 and 2020, to 27TWh. Overall LAWH electricity consumption is increasing in each of the countries at 0.8-1% pa. Gas use is nearly stable, because new boilers are already efficient and offsets the underlying growth caused by more households. With fuel switching on both the demand and supply sides, carbon dioxide emissions should remain stable until 2010 and grow slightly to 22MtC by 2020.

Significant opportunities for savings are available

The Kyoto+ Scenario defines the policies that would save 3.7MtC by 2010 and 6.5MtC by 2020 (Table). The savings result from technologies that are cost-effective for the consumer and come from increased energy efficiency, fuel switching from electricity to gas and from LPG to natural gas in Portugal. Most savings (80%) come from more electrical efficiency, particularly cold appliances, lighting and consumer electronics. Only 5% of the savings come from more efficient gas and the remaining 15% from fuel switching.

Carbon savings in 2010 and 2020 (MtC)

	2010			2020		
	Reference case	Kyoto+ savings	% of RC	Reference case	Kyoto+ savings	% of RC
UK	14.0	2.5	18	15.8	4.7	30
NL	4.2	0.8	19	4.2	1.2	29
PO	1.9	0.4	21	1.8	0.6	34
All 3	20.1	3.7	18	21.8	6.5	30

Emphasis on appliance electrical efficiency benefits all Europeans

With strong support from industry, more efficient electrical appliances are developed. These provide the majority of the savings, from consumer electronics, lighting and cold appliances. Where there is a competing fuel, there is then effective parity between gas and electric appliances, in terms of carbon emissions (ovens, hobs and tumble dryers). There would be no carbon benefits to consumers if they switch fuel. The challenge is to get the efficient electrical appliances cheaper.

Strong EU policies required to deliver savings by 2010

The adoption of a framework directive, by the Commission, would simplify and speed up the process of setting these tough, industry standards and is needed to guarantee the savings in this time scale. Minimum standards deliver savings at a low cost, if they are part of a clear strategy.

Fuel switching – an immediate new potential

Demand-side fuel switching occurs naturally, in both directions: from gas to electric ovens; from electric to gas water heating. There is the potential to enhance lower carbon choices by expanding the gas network (UK and Portugal) and the more intensive use of gas in those households on the network: more use of gas for water heating, cooking and tumble dryers. The emphasis on fuel switching depends on national priorities to reflect the availability of gas, the carbon content of electricity, the avoidance of peak load and the phasing out of nuclear power. Fuel switching is of primary importance in the short-term, whilst more efficient electrical appliances are developed.

Gas use is becoming a focus for European policy
Half of all European households have natural gas and this is expected to grow to over two-thirds by 2020. Provided gas is used at an efficiency of 65% or more, there are carbon savings from the more extensive use of gas in all European countries, except France and Sweden. European policy on domestic gas use will become more important. When space heating is included, gas usage is substantial and the benefits multiply in countries with combined space and water heating boilers (UK and NL). There is a 20% carbon saving when natural gas displaces LPG and more than 40% when electricity is replaced.

National governments could compensate for a lack of EU action, but that is expensive
In the absence of strong EU action on efficiency standards, member states would have to rely more on fuel switching and rebates for efficient electrical appliances to achieve the savings. These policies are slower, more uncertain, result in smaller savings and much more expensive than minimum standards.

Energy labels cannot aid fuel switching
Appliances that can be fired by either gas or electricity (cookers, water heating, tumble dryers) should have separate energy labels that are not directly comparable. This is an interim recommendation, as the whole subject of fuel comparisons needs to be addressed at the EU level, to include household-level renewables. The energy label may have to become a carbon label.

New policies to support the market
New policies that empower the consumer (web based) or the retailer (aggregated purchase) are being developed in Europe. To improve the energy efficiency of hot water systems, installers need to be adequately trained. These are both examples of a new emphasis on education and awareness in market transformation strategies.

Correctly designing policies requires a sophisticated understanding of consumption
Consumption is not the isolated act of an individual – choices about appliances and heating systems take place in complex social, institutional and cultural settings. If more energy and carbon efficient equipment is to get into the home, then this complexity must be recognised and incorporated into the policy process. The policies to deliver the potential savings depend upon a society with shared environmental concerns and commitments and an institutional framework which clearly encourages sustainable choices.

Education through the development of a carbon market
For many countries, like the UK, fuel switching is a contentious subject, but could be tackled through developing a carbon market. This could include carbon budgets for the utilities, to be reduced annually, and information provided to the householder, through an annual carbon bill. A carbon market unites supply and demand-side issues - efficiency, fuel switching and renewables – and clarifies when fuel switching provides a carbon benefit.

Deeper cuts in carbon are required to move towards sustainability
Consensus definitions of sustainable carbon emissions show that even if all the savings identified under Kyoto+ were achieved, the UK, Netherlands and Portugal would not be on the path to sustainability. The Sustainability Scenario demonstrates the need to change perspectives in society and to increase the use of household level renewable energy systems.

Green electricity and renewables need support
Households can reduce their carbon impact through purchasing green electricity and the installation of household-level renewables, mainly solar thermal for hot water. EU policy support is needed in both areas – and with others such as micro CHP - to achieve sustainability. The emphasis on energy efficiency is important now, whilst renewables become cost effective over the medium term.

Significant savings for all EU member states
Across all member states, the Kyoto+ policies affect 82% of all domestic electricity (500 TWh) and 22% of natural gas (260TWh). The adoption of the Kyoto+ Scenario would result in 16MtC savings by 2010 and 29MtC in 2020. As there is likely to be a 14% gap between the growth in emissions and the EU

Kyoto commitment, these savings in LAWH would make an important contribution. A common and co-ordinated approach to minimum standards would seem desirable and would also provide a useful contribution to post-Kyoto debates.

Delay has serious consequences

In 1997, calculations for electrical lights and appliances in the UK established a potential of 2.7MtC by 2010 given immediate action. Two years have passed in which firm EU action has not been taken and the savings available from this sector are now only 2MtC by 2010. Based on past performance, strong EU action can not be guaranteed. With each passing year, the required policy programme becomes even more concentrated if the European Kyoto target is to be achieved.

Strengthening market transformation for a lower carbon future

Market transformation is a powerful strategic approach for delivering significant savings, which can provide real benefits to lower income consumers. The present emphasis on energy efficiency may be insufficient to deliver the required energy conservation or carbon reduction goals of the EU, certainly for targets beyond Kyoto. Energy efficiency is not adequately offsetting the demand created by additional households and a higher standard of living. The focus of market transformation should shift to carbon saving. EU households can benefit later generations by achieving a lower carbon future.

CHAPTER 1: INTRODUCTION

The aim of this report is to present policy solutions to the problem of domestic energy carbon emissions and to identify routes to lower carbon futures for European households. More particularly, for the UK, Netherlands and Portugal, it aims to identify policy opportunities for more efficient use of gas and electricity and fuel switching for lights, appliances and water heating, and to quantify the resultant carbon savings.

To the European Commission and member state governments, this report offers detailed analysis and policy advice on how to ensure that EU households can reduce carbon emissions, thus contributing to reducing further climate change. However, the audience for this report is not governments alone. It will also be useful for anyone wanting to understand household energy demand, and the options for less environmentally damaging modes of consumption in the future. The report also informs business of the likely dimensions of change and the policies under consideration for achieving carbon savings.

1.1   WHY THIS STUDY IS NECESSARY

There is now no serious doubt that anthropogenic greenhouse gas emissions are leading to increased global warming. Since the 1970s, the world has warmed by about 0.15°C per decade, and 1998 was the warmest year on record. The European Union (EU) and national governments have signed up to legally-binding greenhouse gas reduction targets, but do not yet have the policies in place to achieve them. At Kyoto, the member states of the EU agreed jointly to undertake an 8% reduction of six key greenhouse gases from 1990 to 2008-2012. Under EU burden sharing arrangements, the UK reduction target is 12.5%, the Netherlands' is 6% and Portugal is allowed to increase its greenhouse gas emissions by 27%. In addition, the current UK Labour government has committed itself to exceeding the UK Kyoto target and to reduce emissions of carbon dioxide by 20% from 1990 levels by 2010.

However, the policy measures planned and implemented so far will not be sufficient to meet these targets; further action is needed. The need for decisive action is partially the result of failure of previous policies to provide sufficient energy savings, as evidenced by rising household energy demand: "programmes dealing with energy efficiency have had an impact on reducing energy intensity but have not been in themselves sufficient to bring about changes on a scale necessary" (European Commission, DGXVII, 1998). The UK government has published consultation documents on climate change strategy (DETR, 1998), but has not yet produced detailed plans of how the Kyoto target and the 20% saving commitment are to be met. Portugal too has yet to produce a policy response for the domestic sector. Similarly, the European Commission has published a communication on energy efficiency, which while setting out principles, does not suggest detailed policy actions needed to meet the Kyoto targets. This report aims to fill some of those gaps.

The targets set at Kyoto are only a stage towards a less carbon intensive future and more stringent objectives will have to be set and met beyond 2010. The overall reduction required by 2100 may be as much as 90% of current European levels of greenhouse gas emissions if we are to avoid 'dangerous climate change'. There are policies other than energy conservation that will contribute to the Kyoto targets, such as increased use of renewable energy and combined heat and power. However, reduced domestic demand has an important contribution to make both to Kyoto targets, and to savings beyond Kyoto, and this is what this report investigates.

1.2   STRUCTURE OF THE REPORT

This report presents the results of the CADENCE study (**ca**rbon **d**ioxide from **d**omestic **e**quipment: **end**-use efficiency and **c**onsumer **e**ducation), which has been a collaboration between three partner organisations over a period of two years. The three partners are: Environmental Change Institute (ECI), Oxford University, UK (main contractor); ISR, Coimbra, Portugal; Ecofys, Utrecht, the Netherlands.

Whilst overview information for all EU countries is provided, the emphasis of the research has been on all domestic uses of gas and electricity except space heating and cooling in the partner countries.

Chapter 2 presents reference case projections for household energy use and carbon dioxide emissions from lights, appliances and water heating (LAWH) in the UK, Netherlands and Portugal from 1970-2020. The reference case represents the base line for the domestic sector - showing where energy consumption has been in the past and where it is projected to go if the future follows expected trends. The underlying causes of household energy consumption and resulting carbon dioxide emissions including social, economic, ownership, technical and usage trends are explained.

The DECADE model, developed through previous SAVE projects, is used to quantify the results. This is a very detailed model, based on thousands of data points. Although the model provides results up to 2020, energy consumption and carbon dioxide emissions in 2010 are the major focus of this report as Kyoto targets are based around 2010. Modelling gas as well as electricity consumption facilitates analysis of the opportunities for fuel switching from electricity to gas. This could be an important source of carbon savings as gas usually provides the same energy service with lower carbon emissions than electricity, often at lower cost to the consumer.

The potential for reducing carbon dioxide emissions more than in the reference case is examined in Chapter 3. This potential is in the form of:
- more efficient use of electricity;
- more efficient use of gas;
- fuel switching, mainly from electricity to gas.

In addition to large potential efficiency savings, fuel switching from electricity to gas is established as a potentially important means for reducing carbon emissions which has relevance for most, although not all, EU countries. This creates policy opportunities, both in countries where the natural gas network is long established (UK and the Netherlands) and where the fuel is becoming available for the first time (Portugal). Other household-level fuel-switching opportunities that have been investigated include solar water heating, 'heat-fed' laundry appliances and green electricity.

Chapter 4 explains why the actual potential for fuel switching and introduction of more efficient LAWH may not be as large as the theoretical potential identified in Chapter 3. Consumers are bound into complex webs of social and cultural expectations which influence what is considered desirable, acceptable and normal. This may be very different from what is, in theory, economically justified and environmentally beneficial. Also, decisions about specification of water heating equipment in the home, and the availability of particular technologies in the shops are taken by installers, retailers and manufacturers amongst others. This chapter identifies the important actors and relationships in these decisions, and thus the opportunities for intervention. This more realistic understanding of consumers and other decision-makers is key to designing effective policy.

Chapter 5 brings together the current status of market transformation practice and theory for energy efficiency, and discusses the ways in which it could develop to include fuel switching. The purpose is not to be prescriptive about which policy instruments must be used, but rather to explore the different options, their advantages and disadvantages in different situations, and to outline some innovative new approaches. This chapter provides the policy toolkit from which the scenarios in Chapter 6 are developed.

In Chapter 6, a realistic carbon saving scenario that goes beyond the Kyoto targets, based on fully detailed policy measures is described. A detailed timetable for the actions required by national governments and the EU has been provided. Although large and achievable savings are identified, these still fall below the levels needed for sustainable levels of energy consumption. Thus within the framework of sustainability, other possible policy approaches and packages are outlined, together with estimates of the further savings which might be achieved. These approaches include changing lifestyles and use patterns, as well as introducing more innovative technology and new ways of providing consumers with feedback on the impact of their lifestyles.

The implications for the whole of the EU are sketched in Chapter 7 to assist in developing policy priorities. Domestic energy consumption patterns are outlined, allowing simple estimates of savings across the EU to be made, based on country specific knowledge and the very detailed modelling that has been carried out for the three partner countries.

Finally, the results of the research are brought together, the dominant themes identified, and further policy recommendations made in Chapter 8. In addition, priorities for future research are suggested.

1.3   POINTS OF INFORMATION

More detailed background documents related to the CADENCE project are available, both in published form (Country Pictures) and via the ECI web site (www.eci.ox.ac.uk). Throughout the text reference has been made to these where relevant.

A previous report (DECADE, 1997) analysed the potential savings from domestic lights and appliances from 1997-2010. This report evolves from that to also include water heating, which in turn required an analysis of the potential for fuel switching from electricity to gas. Gas is no longer the fuel of a minority of households; by 2020 it will be in over two-thirds of EU homes and will have become an important part of the European climate change policy in the domestic sector. Throughout this report, particular emphasis is placed on these issues.

Prices throughout the report are given either in Euros, or in the original currency and Euros. The exchange rate for the Netherlands is fixed at 1 Euro = 2.2037 NLG, for Portugal 1 Euro = 200.482 PTE. The UK has a floating exchange rate with the Euro, for this report 1 Euro = £0.667.

For numbers, commas are used in this report as separators between thousands.

CHAPTER 2: EXPECTED TRENDS

This chapter presents reference case projections for household energy use and carbon dioxide emissions from lights, appliances and water heating in the United Kingdom, Netherlands and Portugal from 1970-2020. A presentation of the reference case and how it was calculated is the main aim in this chapter. The reference case represents the base line for the domestic sector - showing where energy consumption has been in the past and where it is projected to go if the future follows expected trends. The underlying causes of household energy consumption and resulting carbon dioxide emissions including social, economic, ownership, technical and usage trends are explained. The effects of current policies are included.

The DECADE model, developed through previous SAVE projects, is used to quantify the results. This is a very detailed model, based on thousands of data points. These cannot all be presented, nor can all the assumptions underlying the projections be explained within this report. As a result, key figures for the major appliances are presented in summary format in this chapter while Appendix F presents a more detailed overview of the main inputs and outputs for each major appliance. Although the model provides results up to 2020, energy consumption and carbon dioxide emissions in 2010 are the major focus of this report as Kyoto targets are based around 2010.

This chapter will begin by explaining the modelling methodology (Section 2.1). The discussion is kept brief as it has been developed in detail in previous ECI work. Due to its complexity, water heating methodology is explained in more detail. The chapter will go on to show total energy consumption by the domestic sector first by electrical and then gas LAWHs in section 2.2. The drivers of energy consumption are introduced in Section 2.3 and key numbers for each are provided. Section 2.4 relates energy use to carbon emissions and explains how these have changed over time. Finally, the chapter identifies why the future may not develop as predicted and explains the statistical confidence limits of this run in Section 2.5.

2.1   MODELLING METHODOLOGY

The basis of the projections in this report is a detailed end-use (bottom-up) model, of domestic electricity and gas use in lights, appliances and water heating (LAWH). The model contains information on the ownership, sales, usage and electricity consumption of these household sectors. Linked to this is information about household numbers. The model has been validated wherever possible by using monitored energy consumption data, average household bills and by comparison with total, domestic sector energy consumption. Discussion and consultation with the policy community, manufacturers, retailers and other stakeholders through the UK Market Transformation Programme has assisted in confirming results from the model for electricity use by lights and appliances in the UK. Data limitations (including translation and access to information issues) mean the results for the Netherlands and Portugal are less certain in some cases, however the potential savings described are still robust. Additional details on modelling methodology are given in Appendix O.

2.1.1   Water heating

Modelling hot water energy consumption is more complex than for the other appliance categories and a few words of explanation are provided here to show the assumptions and methodology used. For the UK and the Netherlands the distinction which has been made in this study between energy used for water heating (which is modelled) and energy used for space heating (which is not) is somewhat artificial as both services are often supplied by the same system. This separation was necessitated by the remit of the contract and its short-coming for calculating all potential savings is recognised. Furthermore, the focus in this report is on the efficiency of the boiler / water heater rather than on the efficiency of the entire system. For hot water, efficiency will often be more a consequence of the system than of the boiler efficiency. However, the issue of systems efficiency is immensely complex, as acknowledged by a recent SAVE workshop (NOVEM, 1999), and is beyond the scope of this report. This inevitably means that potential savings from, for example, improved controls, system layout and instantaneous rather than stored water systems will not be quantified. Additionally, due to a lack of adequate data, standing losses from storage tanks are modelled only for domestic electric storage systems and not those from the other water heating appliances.

The terminology for different types of water heating systems used within this study is as follows:

- **combined space and water heating (CSWH)** - is supplied via a natural gas boiler which can be either of the conventional or condensing type, and with storage or instantaneous, giving a total of four combinations. The term 'boiler' preceded by the type is used throughout this report but no distinction between boiler types is made in the model itself, only efficiencies. CSWH can be provided by other fuel sources but these are minor in comparison to natural gas use and are therefore not included in the model.
- **independent water heating (INDP-WH)** – refers to all water heating systems which provide hot water only and make no provision for space heating. These are split into four system types which are modeled separately:
    - natural gas instantaneous water heaters – (G-INST)
    - liquid petroleum gas instantaneous water heaters (Portugal only) (LPG-INST)
    - electric instantaneous water heaters (E-INST)
    - domestic electric stored water heating (DESWH)

Further details about water heating peculiarities in the three countries is provided in Section 2.2.4.

2.1.2 Gas use

With 81% of households connected, the majority of households in the UK have access to and use natural gas for some application. In the Netherlands the connection is even higher with 96% of households while in Portugal only 4% are connected but use of liquid petroleum gas (LPG) is wide-spread. In all three partner countries in this study, most gas consumption is for the production of hot water. Other gas uses modelled are for cooking and tumble drying. Throughout this report gas means natural gas for the UK and the Netherlands and refers to LPG and natural gas in Portugal, unless otherwise specified. These gases are modelled separately due to the difference in emission factors for the two. For Portugal, domestic use of LPG was modelled because of its importance as a fuel source, accounting for about 30% of all household fuels. In the Netherlands and UK LPG is a very minor component of the domestic energy market, 0.3% of total domestic gas in the Netherlands and 1.2% in the UK (derived from DUKES, 1999). Hence only natural gas has been modelled for these countries.

2.1.3 Fuel price

Prices of electricity and gas for households across the EU have been falling in real terms since the mid-1980s. Tax-inclusive natural gas prices have fallen by an average of 30% (measured in terms of purchasing power standards and constant 1990 Euro values) between 1985 and 1996, while electricity prices have fallen by around 11%. Electricity is currently 3.7 times more expensive on a per kWh basis than natural gas: this ratio has remained fairly constant throughout the 1990s (European Commission, 1999). Natural gas prices for domestic consumers are more variable across the EU than electricity prices. This is because of widely varying policies on taxation, subsidies and other policy mechanisms that affect natural gas prices. The introduction of competitive pressure to the electricity and gas markets as a result of European Commission Directives is expected to maintain long-term decreases in the price of both fuels, and particularly that of natural gas.

However, since domestic energy demand is generally inelastic to changes in price, energy prices are not modelled explicitly.

2.2 REFERENCE CASE ENERGY CONSUMPTION

The reference case (RC) describes electricity and gas consumption between 1970 and 1998 and is projected forward to 2020. These projections include estimates of changes in household numbers, ownership, usage and technical changes; and also incorporate the likely effects of policies that have already been defined with a known implementation date.

Electricity consumption per household has been falling in the UK over the past 10 years with a 5% decline projected between 1990 and 2010 (Table 2.1). In the Netherlands and Portugal per household consumption is projected to still rise by 7% and 10% respectively. The fall in the UK can be mainly explained by a shift away from electric water heating to gas, combined with a greater efficiency in cold appliances. Although still rising, the consumption per household in the Netherlands is lower than the UK. The ownership of more efficient appliances explains this. Household consumption is lowest for Portugal, mostly due to the ownership of fewer electrical appliances, even if many of these are more inefficient. By contrast, gas consumption is falling in all three countries with the greatest decline projected in the Netherlands. Improved efficiency in gas boilers and gas INDP-WHs accounts for this decline in all three countries.

In the UK, LAWHs represent 78% of total domestic electricity consumption and 27% of gas consumption in 1998. The remaining 22% and 73% of electricity and gas respectively are used for space heating. Similar splits are found it the Netherlands while the proportion of total consumption is much higher in Portugal because of less space heating.

Table 2.1: Total energy consumption per household by LAWH, RC, 1990-2020

		UK	NL	PO*
kWh electric/hh	**1990**	3867	3,021	2,227
	1998	3505	3,113	2,295
	2010	3670	3,221	2,444
	2020	3631	3,241	2,488
% change 1990-2010		**-5.1%**	**6.6%**	**9.7%**
kWh gas/hh connected	**1990**	3121	3135	2537
	1998	3248	3021	2744
	2010	3137	2603	2607
	2020	2829	2527	2409
% change 1990-2010		**-9.4%**	**-19.4%**	**-5.0%**

*includes both natural gas and LPG

2.2.1   Projections of electricity use, 1970-2020

Despite the fall in household electricity consumption in the UK, national domestic electricity consumption is projected to increase for all three countries (Figure 2. 1). In the UK this increase is expected to be in the order of 9% between 1998 and 2010 and 14% and 12% for the Netherlands and Portugal respectively. An increase in household numbers, with fewer people per household combined with an increase both in ownership of additional appliances, and in appliance use explains this upward trend. Technological progress of appliance efficiency is not expected to be enough to offset this growth. The factors influencing consumption are discussed in detail in Section 2.3.

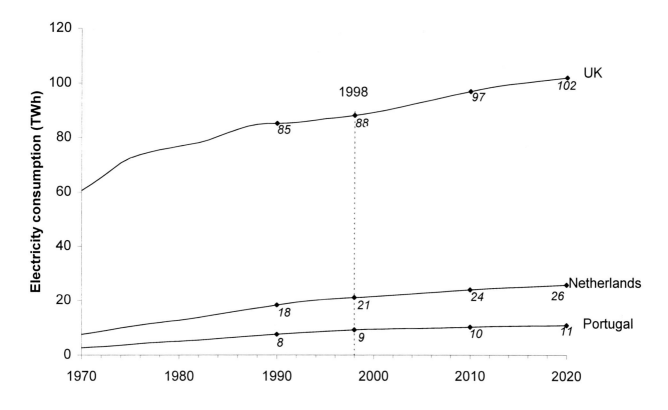

Figure 2. 1: LAWH electricity consumption in the reference case scenario, 1970-2020

2.2.2   Current pattern of electricity use

The patterns of domestic electricity consumption in the three countries reflect, among other things, differences in ownership, lifestyle and technology. Electricity consumption by the cold appliances sector in the UK and the Netherlands is the most similar (with 20%) while for Portugal this sector is by far the most consuming, accounting for over one third of all household consumption. The reason for the greater share can be explained by a lower ownership of other appliances and by the use of more inefficient appliances in Portugal. Lighting is another big consumer in all countries. The biggest difference is in cooking with a share of 14% in the UK but only 4% in the Netherlands and Portugal (Table 2.2). Some reasons for these differences are explained in this chapter, as ownership, usage and technology are considered.

The category 'small cooking' refers to such appliances as toasters, food processors, cooking hoods, electric frying pans etc. Individually these appliances are minor energy consumers but in aggregate can be significant, accounting for 3% consumption in the Netherlands and 1% in the UK. The miscellaneous category, including hair dryers, irons, vacuum cleaners, shavers, answering machines and a list of 13 other small appliances used in the home, makes a similarly small yet important impact. A major, and fast-growing, sector in all countries is consumer electronics (CE), which includes television, videos, audio, computers and especially receiver decoders (RDs or set-top boxes – see a full explanation below). Consumption by this sector in the Netherlands is already at 20% in 1998. The share is expected to increase in all countries.

The stand-by mode in various appliances, especially consumer electronics and microwaves, can consume significant amounts of energy. These are included in Table 2.2. Power demand by stand-by of some appliances is shown in Table 2.8, and additional details presented Appendix F.

Table 2. 2: Total electricity consumption by appliance type, LAWH 1998

	UK		NL		PO	
	GWh	%	GWh	%	GWh	%
Cold	**17,492**	**19.9**	**4,275**	**20.3**	**3,250**	**34.9**
All freezers	11,484	13.1	1,475	7.0	1,037	11.1
Chest freezer	2,013	2.3	-	-	-	-
Fridge-freezer	9,472	10.8	1,590	7.5	1,733	18.6
Refrigerator	3,118	3.6	1,210	5.7	480	5.1
Upright freezer	2,889	3.3	-	-	-	-
Consumer Electronics	**10,419**	**11.9**	**4,449**	**21.1**	**1,213**	**13.0**
Answer machine	138	0.2	60	0.3	-	-
Cassette	29	0.0	121	0.6	7	0.1
Clock	242	0.3	67	0.3	38	0.4
Cordless analogue telephone	144	0.2	-	-	-	-
Cordless digital telephone	27	0.0	-	-	-	-
Hi-Fi	620	0.7	208	1.0	16	0.2
Fax	163	0.2	155	0.7	-	-
Other office equipment	24	0.0	7	0.0	4	0.0
Personal Computer	516	0.6	73	0.3	42	0.5
Printer	57	0.1	17	0.1	5	0.0
TV	5,266	6.0	1,687	8.0	783	8.4
VCR	1,884	2.1	544	2.6	210	2.3
Receiver Decoders						
Cable-analogue	320	0.4	715	3.4	46	0.5
Cable-digital	0.0	0.0	0.0	0.0	0.0	0.0
Satellite-analogue	286	0.3	41	0.2	7.6	0.1
Satellite-digital	47	0.1	0.0	0.0	0.0	0.0
Terrestrial - digital	0.0	0.0	0.0	0.0	0.0	0.0
Cooking	**11,923**	**13.6**	**924**	**4.4**	**378**	**4.1**
Hob	2,973	3.4	268	1.3	123	1.3
Oven	3,391	3.9	129	0.6	186	2.0
Microwave	1,600	1.8	413	2.0	70	0.7
Kettle	3,959	4.5	114	0.5	-	-
Small Cooking	**874**	**1.0**	**661**	**3.1**	**-**	**-**
Lighting	**17,366**	**19.8**	**3,579**	**17.0**	**1,653**	**17.7**
Miscellaneous	**3,218**	**3.7**	**1,854**	**8.8**	**197**	**2.1**
Wet	**11,845**	**13.5**	**3,664**	**17.4**	**956**	**10.3**
Dishwashers	2,170	2.5	338	1.6	265	2.8
Tumble dryers	3,132	3.6	1,512	7.2	139	1.5
Washing machines	5,115	5.8	1,814	8.6	552	5.9
Washer-dryers	1,428	1.6	-	-	-	-
Water Heating	**15,406**	**17.6**	**2,441**	**11.6**	**1,729**	**18.5**
DESWH	12,512	14.3	2,347	11.1	1,729	18.5
E-INST	494	0.6	94	0.4	-	-
Showers	2,400	2.7	-	-	-	-
Total	**87,717**		**21,092**		**9,322**	

An aside about table format

The table above provides a comprehensive overview of the electric appliances included in the model (all gas appliances are shown in Table 2.3). For the remaining tables in this chapter selected appliances are chosen where they provide interesting examples or a good illustration of the situation. In some cases not all appliances listed are modelled for all countries. This is because there is no existence of a particular appliance (in which case the entry is left blank), it was not modelled due to a lack of data (the entry is a hyphen) or in the case of a zero, it indicates the appliance is not owned or used.

Receiver decoders
A word of explanation about digital receiver decoders is provided here, as they are expected to grow considerably (illustrated through ownership in Table 2.6). Digital TV was launched in the UK and other European countries at the end of 1998. The introduction of digital TV means that two types of signals can now be transmitted in three different ways, a total of six combinations. In this report these are denoted as: satellite-analogue, cable-analogue, satellite-digital, cable-digital and terrestrial-digital. The sixth combination is terrestrial-analogue decoding which is integrated within the television itself and is not a separate appliance.

Before the introduction of digital TV, all TV signals were analogue, whether transmitted over terrestrial antennae, cable or satellite. Cable and satellite transmissions required the use of a receiver decoder (often referred to as a set-top box), while terrestrial signals could be received through antennae. These analogue receiver decoders entailed a certain amount of additional power demand when watching cable or satellite TV.

With the introduction of digital TV, a receiver decoder is required for all three modes of transmission. In the model it has been assumed that the growth in digital TV will be fairly rapid and that the changeover from analogue to digital signals will be complete by 2020. By then every household which has a TV will require at least one of these devices.

At the moment it is not clear what the relationship will be between TV ownership and digital receiver decoder ownership. This will depend on whether service providers can agree on platform specifications. At best only one master device will be required per household, capable of servicing multiple TVs (the Master Platform Scenario). At worst each TV will require a receiver decoder for each of the types of transmission required, so that where a household wishes to access cable and satellite as well as terrestrial programmes on a particular TV, multiple receiver decoders will be required (the Multiple Platform Scenario). Somewhere in between these two is the possibility that receiver decoders will be capable of servicing all three modes of transmission, so that only one platform is required per TV (the Common Platform Scenario). It is the Multiple Platform Scenario which has been included in the reference case since this appears to be the most likely scenario at present.

Similar complexities are involved in water heating and a full discussion on the role of water heating is provided in Section 2.2.4. A full list of appliances included in each product group is given in Appendix A.

2.2.3   Projections of gas use, 1970-2020
Despite a rise in the number of households and an increase in ownership of appliances, domestic gas consumption by LAWH is expected to level off in all three countries by 2010 as efficiency improvements in new water heating equipment continue to be introduced to the stock of appliances (Figure 2.2). Details of the projections can be found in Appendix F.

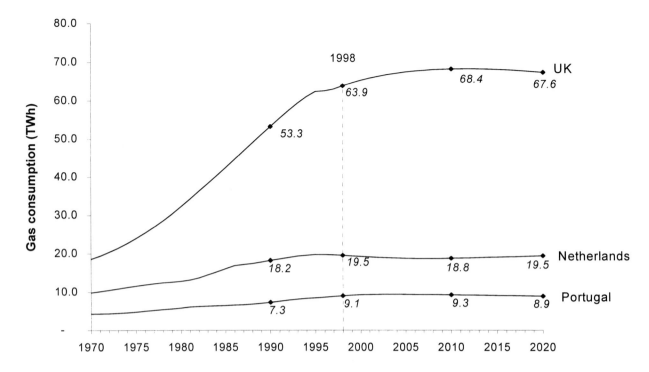

Figure 2. 2: LAWH gas consumption in the reference case scenario, 1970-2020

2.2.4 Current pattern of gas use

The amount of gas used domestically in a country is usually a reflection of the extent of the gas network and the history of gas use. The Netherlands has the most dense natural gas transport and distribution network in the world with 96% of households connected. As a result, gas use is very high, in particular for water heating with almost 90% used for this purpose for LAWH (Table 2.3). Similar trends are seen in the UK, where 81% of households are connected. In Portugal, the gas network is only beginning to be developed and only 4% of the population are currently connected. However, liquid petroleum gas (LPG) is a common source of fuel for water heating and cooking with 85% of the population using LPG for either or both applications. It is expected that LPG will be replaced as the gas network expands. Due to the diversity of hot water production an explanation about the type of systems found in each country is provided below.

Almost 13% of gas is consumed for cooking in the UK, 11% in the Netherlands and 26% in Portugal. Gas hobs take the larger share in consumption over gas ovens in the UK and Netherlands while there is an almost even split between the two in Portugal. Gas consumption is negligible for gas tumble dryers in all three countries.

Table 2.3: Total gas consumption by appliance type, LAWH 1998

	UK		NL		PO*	
	GWh	**%**	**GWh**	**%**	**GWh**	**%**
Cooking	**8,202**	**12.8**	**2,168**	**11.1**	**2,321**	**25.5**
Hob	4,817	7.5	2,111	10.8	1,211	13.3
Oven	3,385	5.3	57	0.3	1,109	12.2
Tumble Dryers	**27**	**0.0**	**4**	**0.0**	**0**	**0.0**
Water Heating	**55,698**	**87.1**	**17,374**	**88.9**	**6,788**	**74.5**
CSWH	49,910	78.1	11,041	56.5	-	-
G-INST	5,789	9.1	6,333	32.4	340	3.7
LPG-INST	-	-	-	-	6,448	70.8
Total	**63,927**	**100.0**	**19,546**	**100.0**	**9,108**	**100.0**

*includes natural gas and LPG

Water heating

In the UK, combined space and water heating (CSWH) systems carry out most water heating, and the majority of these systems are powered by natural gas. Practically the only other system commonly found uses an electric immersion element to heat a cylinder of water directly (referred to as a domestic electric storage water heater – DESWH). Many of these DESWH are largely unused, but 9% of UK households use their DESWH as a back-up system to supply hot water in the summer only when they prefer not to use their gas system. Thus for the UK a distinction is made both between ownership and usage, and between summer-only and year round usage. Hot water is usually supplied via a storage tank in the UK. This contrasts with other European countries where instantaneous water heating (where hot water is supplied instantly with no requirement for a storage facility) has long been the preferred system. The split between electricity and gas energy consumption due to water heating is about 20:80.

In the Netherlands space and water heating is primarily fuelled by gas and 88% of energy for water heating comes from gas. Low level discharge of the exhaust from gas boilers is not permitted in the Netherlands, hence boilers tend to be located in the attic, near the point of discharge (the roof). The Dutch produce much of their hot water through instantaneous appliances, independently of space heating. Condensing instantaneous boilers are very popular in the Netherlands (60% of all new sales) thus hot water does not tend to be stored. There has been a growth in the use of electric close-in boilers - DESWHs (5-10 litres water capacity) for hot water in kitchen and bathroom applications. 18% of households own DESWHs, 50% of which are used to complement hot water from the CSWH system. As a result, ownership of hot water appliances is greater than 100%. Ownership of the dual system can be explained by the unacceptable delays in hot water reaching the taps due to long pipe run from the attic, where the boiler is located.

Portuguese water and space heating differs considerably from both the UK and the Netherlands. This is partly due to the warmer climate and hence lower heating requirements, but also lower economic prosperity. However, the proportion of households with a hot water supply is increasing rapidly: in 1988, 62% of households had a water heating appliance, by 1998 this figure had risen to 86%. Those with no appliance heat their water by wood. The most common fuel used for water heating is LPG by 68% of households in 1998, followed by electricity accounting for 16% and a further 2% using a solar water heater (not modelled). Hot water and heating systems are separate in Portugal. Central space heating is very uncommon in Portugal, but installations of room heaters are rising. CSWH is assumed to reach 5% in 2020 but was less than 1% in 1998.

Ownership and usage patterns of water heating systems in the three countries is provided in Tables 2.6 and 2.7.

2.3   DRIVERS OF ENERGY CONSUMPTION

As stated previously, energy consumption is influenced by household numbers, ownership, usage, technology and policy. The DECADE model uses these to build the reference case. In this section these drivers are presented and key figures introduced:

- household numbers (Section 2.3.1);
- ownership of appliances and water heating equipment (2.3.2);
- usage (2.3.3);
- technology (2.3.4) and;
- current EU and national policy and its effects on energy efficiency (2.3.6 – 2.3.8)

Household numbers are rising in all three countries and thus represent a major driver of increasing energy consumption. Ownership of energy consuming products is also rising, and new technologies enjoying rapid uptake, such as digital consumer electronics, represent one of the major threats to meeting energy conservation targets. Increased usage due to changing lifestyles and rising service requirements is another driver for increased energy consumption. However, this is not universally true, and some changes to usage patterns are reducing energy consumption, an example being the Europe-wide trend to lower temperature use of washing machines.

The major policy approach, which is currently being used to counter-act all these drivers, is to improve the energy efficiency of end-use. As will be demonstrated in Chapter 3, significant carbon emission reductions can be achieved through efficiency improvements beyond those already being made. However, these are expected to be insufficient to challenge the major sources of increasing energy demand, and may face problems in meeting longer term carbon reduction targets (see Chapter 6 for further discussion).

2.3.1   Population and households

Population is growing in the UK, Netherlands and Portugal, and as for all EU countries, the number of households has been growing faster than the population due to decreasing household size (Table 2.4). Between 1990 and 2010 households in the UK will have increased by 16%, in the Netherlands by 21% and Portugal by 24%. The decline in average household size is directly linked to women having fewer children and the age structure of the population changing as a consequence of lower fertility and people living longer. In addition, the differentiation in living arrangements and changes in marriage behaviour have also resulted in smaller households. The changing number and size of households will have far-reaching consequences for the future demand for services such as housing, energy and water. Household projections for all three countries are presented in Appendix S.

Table 2.4: Predicted number of households, 1990-2020 (millions)

	UK	*NL*	*PO*
1990	22.8	6.1	3.4
1998	24.3	6.7	3.9
2010	26.4	7.4	4.2
2020	28.1	7.9	4.4
% increase 1990 to 2010	**15.8**	**21.3**	**23.5**

The percentage of the population of all EU countries living alone has been increasing since the 1960s. In 1996, one-person households accounted for 28% of all EU households, compared to just 22% in 1991. The trends towards smaller households and increasing proportions of one-person households are expected to continue into the future, at least for Northern European member states, and to gather momentum up to the year 2010 (Eurostat, 1998).

Household size and energy consumption

Both declining household size and increasing numbers of one-person households are likely to hinder efforts to reduce energy-related carbon dioxide emissions. Energy consumption per person increases as household size decreases; one-person households in particular have much higher energy consumption per person than larger households (Table 2.5). Average energy consumption per household may show little or no increase (as in the Netherlands in the period 1990-1995), however the annual energy consumption per person has increased due to the decreasing household size (Vringer *et al.*, 1995).

Table 2.5: Scale effects of household size on the use of energy (one-person household = 100)

Household size	NL electricity	NL gas	UK electricity	UK gas
1	100	100	100	100
2	149	154	137	129
3	180	192	165	142
4	216	231	180	156
5	236	262	192	175

Source: NL - Noorman and Schoot Uiterkamp, 1998; UK – analysis of EHCS, 1996 data

The detailed energy needs and consumption patterns of one-person households are not sufficiently understood to determine whether there is an opportunity for policy intervention to narrow this gap. For example, there might be an opportunity to encourage the design of appliances which are more suited to one-person households, e.g. smaller cold appliances and ovens, which enable them to meet their needs using less energy. Work has been undertaken by the Swedish National Board for Industrial and Technical Development, looking at the development and marketing of smaller washing machines geared to the one-person household (NUTEK, 1995). However, much of the energy consumption will be providing basic services such as a heated, well-lit living space, the requirements for which rise fairly slowly as households increase in number (and physical size). Also some appliances, such as TVs and VCRs, whose use would normally be shared, will result in more energy consumption per person in the one-person household, though individualisation within households (i.e. members of households acting independently) is producing the same effect.

2.3.2   Ownership of appliances

The ownership levels of appliances are key to understanding current energy consumption and projecting energy use into the future. Appliance ownership has grown over time in all three partner countries, and although ownership of some appliances appears to have reached saturation, other sectors are still growing. Dishwashers are expected to be a growth area in all three countries over the next 20 years with ownership almost doubling in Portugal. Microwave ownership is also expected to grow strongly Portugal with less increase in the UK and the Netherlands (Table 2.6). Portugal is expected to show the strongest growth for many appliances as prosperity in this country increases. The consumer electronics sector is expected to show the most ownership growth in all three countries. TV ownership is already well beyond the 100% level due to multiple ownership - sum of TV1 , TV2 and TV3 in Table 2.6. Cold appliances have also reached over 100% ownership (due to multiple ownership in many households) but are not projected to increase into the future.

A natural tendency to fuel switching from electricity to gas for some appliances is in evidence and expected to continue in the UK and Portugal over the next 20 years. In the UK the trend is towards more gas CSWH systems and away from DESWHs, while at the same time gas hobs are becoming more popular and enjoying wider use than electric ones. However, this fuel switch to gas hobs is offset by a similar increase in electric ovens away from gas. In Portugal, with the spread of the natural gas network, gas use in general will increase with a shift from LPG to natural gas. Gas use for water heating will increase from 68% in 1998 to 72% in 2020. The proportion of gas use for cooking is not expected to change, but there will be a shift away from LPG. As pointed out in Section 2.2.4 DESWH ownership and use are different in the UK and the distinction for summer-use and all-year use is made in the table below.

The opportunities for further fuel-switching are apparent when ownership of gas appliances are compared to the levels of those connected to the natural gas network. For instance in the UK, 81% have gas, 78% use gas for water heating, 54% for cooking and less than 1% has a gas tumble dryer.

In addition to projecting ownership of established appliances, there is the question of increased ownership of appliances that have only just been introduced to the market; key examples would be receiver decoders (RDs). RDs have only been introduced on the market in 1999 but ownership is expected to increase rapidly beyond 100% in all three countries by 2020, as digital broadcasting becomes standard.

Table 2.6: Ownership of selected goods, RC, 1998 and 2020 (% households)

	UK		NL		PO*	
	1998	2020	1998	2020	1998	2020
Consumer Electronics						
Cable-RD	11	40	92	100	10	20
Satellite-RD	17	25	6	15	18	50
Terrestrial-RD	0	192	0	189	0	183
TV1	98	100	98	99	99	99
TV2	58	70	57	65	43	64
TV3	18	22	15	25	12	20
VCR1	82	90	84	90	52	90
VCR2	12	25	10	24	3	8
Cooking						
Hob - electric	46	43	15	15	12	12
Hob - gas	54	57	85	85	85	85
Oven - electric	57	69	64	56	20	20
Oven - gas	41	31	20	20	77	77
Microwave	77	85	72	75	21	39
Wet						
Dishwashers	22	31	25	33	17	33
Dryers - electric	35	35	56	62	8	25
Dryers - gas	0.3	0.5	0.1	0.3	0	0
Washing machines	77	80	95	96	81	95
Washer-dryers	15	15	-	-	-	-
Water Heating						
CSWH	70	80	57	65	0	5
DESWH-ownership	63	57	18	18	16	16
DESWH-all year use	17	14	-	-	-	-
DESWH-summer use	9	8	-	-	-	-
E-INST	1	1	6	6	-	-
G-INST	8	5	36	28	3	25
LPG-INDP	-	-	-	-	65	42

*includes natural gas and LPG

2.3.3 Usage patterns

For most appliances, energy consumption depends largely on the usage patterns of householders, the key exception being cold appliances, which are permanently switched on. The usage patterns of selected UK appliances and their expected development by 2020 are shown below (Table 2.6), data for the Netherlands and Portugal are not presented simply because they are very similar in most cases. For washing machines and dishwashers the number of cycles at different temperature settings (40°C, 60°C and 90°C for washing machines and 55°C and 65°C for dishwashers) need to be factored into the calculation of total energy consumption. Although the number of clothes washes is expected to stay constant, there has been a decrease in the number of washes at 90°C, helping contribute to a decrease in energy consumption in the wet sector. This trend is expected to continue in all three countries. Cooking appliances are also expected to be used less in future, particularly ovens. By contrast, TV viewing is expected to increase to 7.3 hours/day from today's 6.5 hours in the UK (Table 2.7), with a similar trend in the Netherlands and Portugal.

Table 2.7: Usage patterns of selected LAWH, UK, 1998, per owning household

			RC		
		1990	**1998**	**2020**	**units**
Consumer Electronics					
	Terrestrial digital - on	0	0	7.3	hours/day
	Terrestrial digital - standby	0	0	16.7	hours/day
	Satellite analogue - on	1.3	1.3	1.1	hours/day
	Satellite analogue - standby	22.7	22.7	22.9	hours/day
	TV-on mode (all)	5.6	6.5	7.3	hours/day
	TV standby (first TV only)	6.1	6.1	6.1	hours/day
	VCR-on	1.3	1.3	1.3	hours/day
	VCR-standby	22.7	22.7	22.7	hours/day
Cooking					
	Oven – electric & gas	280	223	142	uses/yr
	Hob – electric & gas	408	369	369	uses/yr
	Microwave	80	80	80	uses/yr
Lighting					
	All lighting	18	20	24	bulbs/hh
Wet					
	Dishwasher	255	251	241	cycles/yr
	Tumble dryer	145	148	148	cycles/yr
	Washing machine	273	274	274	cycles/yr
Water Heating					
	All - main provision	103	103	103	litres/day
(NL only)	DESWH-secondary provision	50	50	50	litres/day
(NL only)	G-INST secondary provision	12	12	12	litres/day

Water-heating use is calculated by reference to the amount of hot water demanded. The figures for main provision given in Table 2.7 are taken from a European study on DESWHs completed in 1996. 'Main provision' refers to water heating systems used to provide water for all uses. Average daily hot water usage of 103 litres is applicable for all systems in the UK, where all hot water needs are assumed to come from one system. In the Netherlands, however, DESWHs are often used as a secondary water-heating source, complementing the CSWH system. In order to reflect this difference in use, the number of litres supplied was varied in the model. For a DESWH used as the main means of water provision, 103 litres are delivered on average whilst for a DESWH used as secondary source, only 50 litres are assumed to be delivered (to the kitchen and bathroom sinks for instance). A similar distinction in use is made for gas instantaneous appliances in the Netherlands. About 6% of these are used as secondary water heating sources supplying about 12 litres per day. The remaining 94% are used as the main source and a use of 103 litres was modelled. Constant figures have been used in all three countries through time. Very little measured data exists on households' hot water demand and thus there remains a great deal of uncertainty about these figures. A current EU study on water heating is expected to provide improved data.

2.3.4   Technology

Technological improvement in energy efficiency is seen as the key to decreasing energy consumption in domestic LAWH. Such improvements are the target of most policy measures undertaken by the EU and member states. Progress made in energy efficiency, whether by autonomous development or policy actions, has been factored into the reference case of the model. Past and future technology is illustrated for the UK below (Table 2.8). Samples of the most interesting and up-to-date developments are provided here, with additional details available in Appendix F. As many of the products are sold EU-wide, the figures are very similar, if not the same for the Netherlands and Portugal.

Table 2.8: Power demand / unit energy consumption in average new LAWH, RC 1990, 1998, 2020

	Av. New		RC	
	1990	**1998**	**2020**	**Units**
Cold				
Chest freezers	447	409	278	kWh/yr
Fridge-freezers	628	584	416	kWh/yr
Refrigerators	312	239	171	kWh/yr
Upright freezers	475	403	292	kWh/yr
Consumer electronics				
Satellite digital - on		16	30	Watt
Satellite digital - stby		16	9	Watt
TV - on mode	77	69	80	Watt
TV - standby	9.0	4.8	2.2	Watt
VCR - on	32.8	22.1	20.0	Watt
VCR - standby	12.2	5.9	3	Watt
Cooking				
Oven - electric	1.07	1.00	1.00	kWh empty test new
Oven - gas	1.515	1.515	1.515	kWh brick test new
Hob - electric	0.72	0.72	0.72	kWh/use new
Hob - gas	1.00	1.00	1.00	kWh/use new
All lighting	702	715	841	kWh/hh stock
Wet				
Washing machine	1.34	1.21	1.04	kWh/cycle
Dishwasher	1.87	1.46	1.35	kWh/load
Water Heating				
CSWH	69.8	74.3	86.7	seasonal efficiency %*

* as defined in SAP 1998

A few key examples of increasingly efficient technology are:

- Cold appliances, which have been increasing in efficiency in the UK through measures such as increased insulation and better matched compressors. This improvement was aided by the introduction of labels in 1995. Minimum efficiency standards in September 1999 and a revised energy label (around 2002) mean that the average consumption of fridge-freezers sold in 2010 is expected to be even lower

- Wet appliances are expected to continue to become more efficient as manufacturers produce, retailers stock and consumers purchase and use more efficient appliances

- Lighting efficiency has been improving due to the increasing ownership of CFLs, a trend which is projected to continue, however energy consumption per household is increasing because people are owning and using more bulbs (Table 2.7)

- Gas boilers have improved in efficiency, and will continue to do so in the RC. The average new boiler in the UK has a (SAP) seasonal efficiency of 74%, this is expected to increase to 87% in 2020 (see Glossary for explanation of these units, and other measures of boiler efficiency). Campaigns to promote condensing boilers in the NL mean that a relatively high level of efficiency is already present (81.4%) and assumed to reach 85% by 2005. The EU Boiler Efficiency Directive (see Table 2.9) has already eliminated the least efficient boilers on the market.

As well as offering opportunities for savings through efficiency, new technology can also create demand for increased energy consumption. A key example is the introduction of digital broadcasting technologies – the service providers' demand for 24 hour access to set-top boxes at a higher standby level will mean significant increases in domestic electricity consumption. Television on-mode consumption is also expected to rise (69 watts in 1998 to 80 watts in 2020), due to the tendency to wider screens and enhanced audio-visual features. Reference case technology and potential for efficiency improvements is revisited in Chapter 3, Table 3.2.

2.3.5 EU policy

The EU is the source of the most influential policy for domestic LAWH (see Appendix D). Its major focus is on technological efficiency, and not the usage or ownership patterns which are also important in determining energy consumption. The process of EU policy making is outlined in Chapter 5, along with the theory of market transformation and a description of the role of each policy instrument. Here, the main policy instruments which have been introduced and are currently planned are simply described (Table 2.9). Only those which have been finally agreed have been included in the modelling of expected developments in technology in the reference case scenario.

Table 2.9: Summary of European policy instruments (current and under negotiation*)

Sector	Sub-sectors covered	Instrument	Directive	Minimum efficiency level/maximum power demand	In force† /target date
Multiple		Framework legislation for energy labels	92/75		1.1.1994
Cold		1st label	94/2		1.1.1995
		2nd label*	-		2002
		1st minimum standard	96/57	C except for chest freezers where it is E	3.9.1999
		2nd minimum standard*	-	Possibly additional 20% over 1992 baseline	2003
Wet	Washing machines	1st label	95/12		1.10.1996
		2nd label*	-		2002
		Industry agreement	-	D (with minor exceptions) C	1.1.1998 1.1.2000
		Industry agreement*	-	5% reduction from 1.04kWh per wash-load (1996 baseline)	2001
	Tumble dryers	Label	95/13		1.10.1996
	Washer-dryers	Label	96/60		1.1.1998
	Dishwasher	1st label	97/17		1.8.1999
		2nd label*	-		2004
		Industry agreement *	-	10 place settings: D; < 10 place settings: E 10 place settings: C; < 10 place settings: D	1.1.2001 1.1.2005
Consumer electronics	TV and VCR	Industry agreement	-	Standby: max cons. 10W; fleet average 6W Standby: fleet average 3W	1.1.2000 1.1.2009
	Audio	Industry agreement	-	Standby: 5W Standby: 3W Standby: 1W	1.1.2001 1.1.2004 1.1.2007
	Digital receiver decoders	Industry agreement	-	Standby: 9W for stand-alone, 10W for integrated digital receiver decoder Standby: new targets to be defined in 2003	1.1.2003 2005
	External power suppliers	Industry agreement *	-	No-load: 0.3W and < 75W: 1W No-load: 0.3W and < 75W: 0.5 W No-load: 0.3-0.75 depending on power output	1.1.2001 1.1.2003 1.1.2005
Lighting	Lamps	Label	98/11		1.1.2001
	Fluorescent ballasts	Minimum standard		C B2 A3 or B1 depending on the market situation	1.1.2002 1.1.2005 1.1.2008
Cooking	Ovens	Label*	-		2001 or later
Water heating	Boilers	Minimum standard	92/42	eliminated the least efficient boilers on the market	1.1.1998
	Electric storage heaters	Label*	-		2001 or later
		Industry agreement *			2000-2002

† In force indicates the date on which the provisions should be in force in the member states, e.g. the date from which energy labels should be on the appliances in the shops

* = under negotiation or development; provisional details given where available but these may change

Effects of policy

Chapter 5 includes a comprehensive discussion about the complexity of measuring and predicting the effects of policy actions on energy efficiency. For example, energy labels are enabling policies that allow other actions to be undertaken. Their value cannot be solely measured by energy savings that result directly from their imposition. Nevertheless, assumptions based on the best evidence available have to be made for the purposes of modelling the reference case, and some examples of these are summarised below (Table 2.10).

Table 2.10: Estimate of effects in UK of some recent and forthcoming EU policy instruments

Appliance group	Type	Policy instrument	Estimated rate of change prior to policy	Effect of policy instrument
Cold	all	energy label	difficult to estimate as data poor prior to label introduction	adding to background rate of efficiency improvement
	refrigerators	minimum standard	Approximately 1.5% per annum (excluding effects of change in sales pattern)	minor – little different from what would have been expected, these already efficient in the UK
	fridge-freezer	minimum standard	reduction of energy consumption of 0.9% per annum, 1989-1998	major - change average new from 580 kWh in 1998 to 500 kWh in 2000
	chest freezer	minimum standard	reduction of energy consumption of 1.1% per annum, 1989-1998	major - change average new from 410 kWh in 1998 to 350 kWh in 2000
	upright freezer	minimum standard	reduction of energy consumption of 1% per annum, 1989-1998	major - change average new from 400 kWh in 1998 to 360 kWh in 2000
Lighting	all	energy label	increasing sales of CFLs – partially as a result of national policies	little – consumers can already distinguish the most efficient bulbs
	fluorescent	ballast standard	electronic ballast sales increasing at the expense of magnetic	none – the rate of change is not significantly different from that expected

The modelled response of cold appliances to the minimum standard varies in the Netherlands and Portugal due the differences in their markets. The Netherlands market prior to minimum standard was already more efficient than the UK, whilst the Portuguese refrigeration appliances were as inefficient as those in the UK. All other appliances are relatively similar in nature.

2.3.6   UK policy

As yet, there are no official sector targets for energy efficiency, energy conservation or carbon emissions reduction in the UK, only the total of 20% carbon dioxide reduction by 2010 for the nation as a whole (and a legally binding target of 12.5% for a basket of greenhouse gases). Similar to developments at the Community level, there was a shift away from the emphasis on energy conservation in the 1970s to energy efficiency in the 1980s and 1990s, and efficiency remains the focus of EU and UK policy (see Appendices D and E). The distinction between energy conservation and efficiency represents a shift in emphasis: using less energy by any means (either through efficiency measures or through lowered consumption and potentially reduced service) to maintaining the same service with lower energy consumption.

At the national level, LAWH efficiency instruments are mainly confined to subsidies and information provision in various forms. A number of programmes and legal instruments have been created to promote energy efficiency in the UK. Their implementation is usually delegated to institutions other than central government. For LAWH the most important of these institutions are the privatised energy utilities, the Energy Saving Trust (EST) and local government.

Funding for subsidy schemes is provided via a levy of £1 (1.5 Euros) per electricity customer per year, which is due to be increased to £1.20 (1.8 Euros) per year from April 2000, and also extended to gas customers. Clearly the low level of charge is not intended to send a price signal to the consumer. The schemes funded in this manner are known as Standards of Performance (SOP) schemes, and include insulation and heating as well as LAWH efficiency measures. LAWH subsidy schemes run by the EST in recent years are summarised in Table 2.11.

The most recent EST cold appliance rebate scheme was run during summer 1999, through which almost 45,000 units of A-C rated refrigeration appliances were sold. This scheme is assessed in detail in section 4.3, the full market effects are not yet known.

Table 2.11: Summary of recent UK LAWH subsidy schemes

Appliance	No. subsidised/year	Scale of Programme	Comments
Cold	Approx. 40,000 per year since mid 1990s	1.5% of new sales	Some subsidies through the Fridge-savers scheme for low-income households, which provides a new efficient refrigerator or fridge-freezer (not necessarily A rated) very cheaply in exchange for an old working one.
Washing machines	No more than 8000 by mid-1999	0.5% of new sales	
CFLs	7.9m by March 1998. 2.6m more expected by end 2000, giving a total of 10.5m	40-47% of CFL acquisitions	Up to 47% of CFLs in UK households were provided via subsidy schemes by March 1998. In practice about 40% of those in use.
Condensing boilers	6000 (1996-97), 9200 in 1997-98 and 27,000 installations to 2000	2% of boiler market in 1997-98	Overall market share of condensing boilers was approximately 5% in 1998.

Sources: EST(1998); EST (1999); Ofgem (1999)

While a third of the first round of SoP (1994-1998) expenditure went on domestic energy efficient lighting, only 7% went on appliances, most of which was spent on cold appliances (www.est.org.uk.). The resulting scale of the schemes is such that only the lighting subsidy has had an appreciable effect on a national level.

2.3.7 Dutch policy

By contrast, the Dutch policy approach to CO_2 reductions is more explicit in terms of setting carbon reduction goals (see Appendix L). In the Energy Savings Action Programme 1999-2002 of the Ministry of Economic Affairs, the ambitious level for energy efficiency improvement of appliances in households is set at 1.8% per year for the period 1995 to 2010.

The energy distribution companies adopted an Environmental Action Plan (MAP) in 1991, with the objective of reducing CO_2 emissions caused by energy consumption by 3% by 2000. The measures undertaken included stimulating energy conservation in homes, utility buildings and industry, and promoting more efficient production techniques (e.g. co-generation and sustainable energy). To finance this, most energy companies have applied the MAP levy since 1991 on all domestic and small business consumers. The MAP-levy will cease at the end of 2000.

A new environmental tax, the REB, was applied first in 1996 in a limited fashion, excluding most domestic consumers from paying the tax. In 1999 all energy users were brought under the same progressive tax regime. The REB is partly returned in reduced income tax – i.e., not all the income is used to finance efficiency measures. The collection of REB and the payment of the energy contribution will be carried out by the energy companies. Energy efficient domestic appliances have been subsidised from 1 November 1999, with money raised from REB. The budget for the domestic sector is over 100 million Euro per year for A-label appliances and efficiency measures in building (e.g., insulation measures). Approximately 25 million Euro is expected to be spent on appliances, at the levels per appliance shown below (Table 2.12). This level of expenditure is approximately six times that in the UK on a per household basis. Other subsidies may cease as a result of the introduction of the REB appliance subsidy.

Table 2. 12: Appliance subsidies in the Netherlands, 1999-2000

Household appliances	*Subsidy*	*(in Euros)*
A-rated refrigerators, fridge-freezers, dishwashers, washing machines	fl 100	45
A-rated washer-dryer	fl 450	200
A-rated electric tumble dryer and any gas tumble dryer	fl 350	160
purchase of two or more different appliances from the above list at same time	bonus fl 50	23

Other subsidies are currently in force and the amounts involved can change each year. Bodies awarding subsidies include power distribution companies, government agencies and local authorities.

2.3.8 Portuguese policy

Beyond implementing EU legislation on standards and labelling, little has been done in Portugal to support the purchase of more efficient lights and appliances. A new regulatory framework for the electricity sector, published in 1998, allows utilities to recover in rates the costs associated with the implementation of DSM programmes promoting the penetration of energy efficient equipment. The effects are not yet quantified. There are currently no environmental energy taxes in Portugal; no additional effect, above that of EU policy, has been modelled for the reference case for Portugal.

2.4 REFERENCE CASE CARBON DIOXIDE EMISSIONS

The reference case of energy consumption for each country was given earlier in Section 2.2. These can be converted to carbon dioxide emissions by multiplying the energy values by conversion factors. The electricity carbon intensity factors will change through time (Section 2.4.1). Adding the estimated gas and electricity appliance carbon emissions provide the reference case emissions (Figure 2.3).

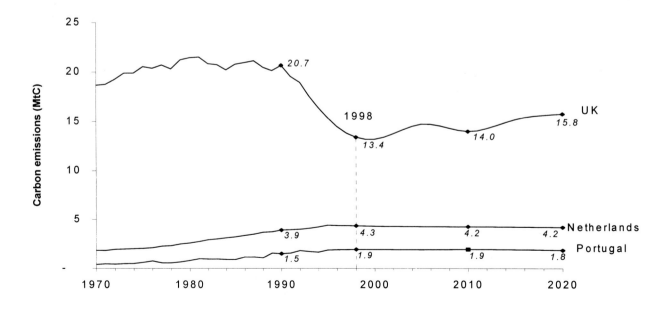

Figure 2. 3: Carbon emissions from gas and electric LAWH, 1970 – 2020

Increased energy consumption in all three countries will mean that carbon emissions are expected to increase between 1990 and 2020 in Portugal and the Netherlands. As shown in Table 2.13, this will be an increase of 6% in the Netherlands and 22% in Portugal. In the UK, this increase in energy consumption will not result in increased emissions between 1990 and 2010 due to the large decrease in the carbon content of electricity in the early 1990s. In fact household emissions from LAWH are projected to fall by 24%. When calculated by household, emissions are highest for the Netherlands with 6.45 tonnes of carbon in 1998 and lowest in Portugal. The lower emissions for Portugal are explained by fewer appliance ownership (Table 2.6). Carbon intensity is also important in explaining emission levels in each country and these are discussed in more detail below (Section 2.4.1)

LAWH emissions as a percentage of total household domestic emissions account for 43% in the UK in 1998, 39% in the Netherlands (in 1997) and almost 100% in Portugal (in 1996). The remaining emissions are almost entirely accounted for by space heating.

Table 2.13: Carbon emissions from LAWH, 1990-2010

	UK	NL	PO
% change in emissions 1990-2010	-24	+6	+22
% of total domestic gas + elec. Emissions*	43	39	99
Tonnes of carbon for LAWH/household, 1998	5.52	6.45	5.05

*This figure is for 1998 in the UK, 1997 in the Netherlands and 1996 in Portugal

2.4.1   Carbon intensity of electricity and gas

The carbon intensity of electricity depends primarily on the fuel sources for generation and the efficiency of converting fossil fuels into electricity. It differs considerably between countries (see Table 5.4 for EU overview) and varies over time as the fuel mix for generation changes (Table 2.14)

At present, electricity in the UK is more than twice as carbon intensive as gas, despite the decline of carbon content of electricity over the past 20-30 years. The reason for the decline since the 1970s is widespread introduction of nuclear power and, more recently, of combined-cycle gas turbine generation plants and subsequent decline in the use of coal. The fluctuations shown in Figure 2.3 from 2000 onward are due to the retirement of older nuclear plants and the projection that no new nuclear plant is built. If the government target of 10% renewable generation by 2010 were met, which seems unlikely, carbon intensity would reduce further. The future carbon intensity of electricity is also expected to decline in the Netherlands and Portugal, due to combined-cycle gas turbine generation as shown in Table 2.14. The carbon intensity of electricity in the UK varies by about 10% between the general tariff (all 24 hours) and the off-peak tariff (mainly 7 hours at night). Although much of the water heating is by off-peak tariff, the standard conversion factor has been used by all.

Table 2. 14: Carbon intensity of delivered gas and electricity, 1990-2020, kg carbon/kWh

Fuel	Year	UK	NL	PO
Electricity	**1990**	0.21	0.16	0.14
	1998	0.11	0.16	0.15
	2000	0.11	0.15	0.15
	2010	0.11	0.14	0.14
	2020	0.12	0.12	0.12
Natural Gas	**all years**	0.05	0.05	0.05
LPG	**all years**	0.06	0.06	0.06

For natural gas there is a standard conversion factor to convert the delivered energy figure into a carbon dioxide emission figure. The figure for LPG is greater than for natural gas, so converting to natural gas reduces carbon emissions by at least 20%, even in the same system. The modification is minor, so new appliances are not needed.

2.5 DIFFERENT FUTURES

The reference case represents the most likely future development in energy consumption and carbon emissions to 2020, given the present course of policy and underlying factors. However, clearly the future could be different from the projections presented here for a variety of reasons, many of which lie outside the realm of energy modelling. These are discussed in Section 2.5.2. Firstly, however, the confidence limits on the projections based on the certainty of input data are discussed.

2.5.1 Statistical errors on projections

Energy consumption has been estimated through time using a stock model. These estimates, known as point estimates, are not exact and are subject to the error of the input data (i.e. ownership, specific energy consumption, life-span and usage of appliances). And, of course, these inputs also become less certain, have a larger margin of error, when they are projected into the future.

The confidence limits on the estimated consumption values have been calculated by employing a Monte Carlo method. This technique allows confidence limits to be estimated where the certainties of input variables are known. Error ranges (or more correctly, probability density functions - distributions of the likelihood of the variables' true values) are specified for the average new consumption of a machine sold through time, the ownership through time and the average life span of each appliance. Using a random number generator all the input variables are chosen (from the probability density function) and the consumption estimated using the stock model. This process is repeated many times (greater than 1000) and the results are used to describe a (probability likelihood) distribution of the estimated consumption, the mean of which is the point estimate (if there are normal distributions on the input variables). The standard deviation of this distribution is used to determine the confidence level.

The standard errors on the estimates of both historical data and future projections are smallest for the UK and become larger for the Netherlands and larger still for the Portugal where the data becomes increasingly uncertain.

2.5.2 Alternative scenarios

The projections modelled in the CADENCE reference case could be substantially different if social, economic and technical trends vary greatly from what is indicated today, namely if household size, appliance ownership, usage patterns and technological developments are substantially different. Research already exists which explores different possible futures. For example, the UK's national Foresight Programme has developed four scenarios of environmental futures (OST, 1999). Broadly similar scenarios emerged from a European Commission funded modelling exercise (Weber and Perrels, forthcoming).

The Foresight scenarios have been framed in the context of two basic dimensions of change: social values and governance systems. The social values dimension takes account of policy-making priorities and patterns of economic activity, including consumption behaviour and varies from "consumerism" to "community". The governance system dimension represents the geographical structure of political authority and decision-making, the two extremes are characterised as globalisation and regionalisation. These dimensions are taken as axes which define the four scenarios: World Markets (globalisation and consumerism), Global Sustainability (globalisation and community), Provincial Enterprise (regionalisation and consumerism) and Local Stewardship (regionalisation and community).

Depending on the direction of future development, energy consumption and carbon emissions in the reference case can be considerably different from what has been presented in this chapter. Approximate calculations show that in a World Market scenario for instance, LAWH carbon dioxide emissions in the UK by 2020 would be 50% higher than those in a Global Sustainability world. Hence the RC projected here is a possible middle case. A discussion of these alternative scenarios is presented in Appendix I.

2.6   CONCLUSIONS

The reference case provides an indication of the future and without further policy action LAWH electricity and gas consumption is expected to increase significantly by 2010. Consumer demand for energy continues to grow, at national, household and per capita levels. Despite strongly increasing energy use, the UK carbon emissions will not increase because of supply side switching to gas and nuclear, thereby achieving its Kyoto target for this sector. However, not having the advantage of steeply falling carbon emissions per unit of electricity, the Netherlands will have difficulty achieving its target. Portugal is permitted significant growth and is within this range.

Efficiency improvements, often driven by EU and national policy, are expected to achieve savings in a number of sectors including wet and cold. In the UK, the main policy activity as far as energy efficiency in LAWH is concerned has been in lighting. Dutch government policy in relation to LAWH appears more advanced and coherent than that of the UK or Portugal. However, known policies and technological improvements are insufficient to offset the growth in demand resulting from more households, higher ownership levels and increased usage. The growth in demand for electricity is greater than that projected for gas, because of the widening range of electrical appliances coming onto the market, particularly consumer electronics. The rise in digital technology and the domestication of the PC and the internet, suggests this sector requires urgent action to curb the expected growth in electricity demand

There is an underlying fuel-switching tendency towards natural gas for water heating and cooking appliances (especially hobs) in the UK and Portugal, which contributes towards decreased domestic primary energy consumption and carbon emissions. In the Netherlands, substantial fuel-switching has already occurred.

The growth of energy demand despite the continuing and strong emphasis on energy efficiency may indicate that future policies may have to focus on energy and carbon conservation directly. Chapter 6 explores how this shift in emphasis might look, however, in the next chapter possible savings through increased efficiency and fuel-switching will be presented.

CHAPTER 3: POTENTIAL CARBON SAVINGS

This chapter will identify options for reducing carbon emissions in relation to the Reference Case Scenario. The opportunities can be classified as:
- more efficient use of electricity;
- more efficient use of gas;
- fuel switching to lower carbon fuels.

Initially the savings from the purchase of more energy efficient electric and gas appliances will be identified, and then fuel-switching savings will be added to estimate potential carbon emissions reductions. However, other ways of reducing carbon emissions will also be outlined.

The technical options for switching from electricity to natural gas are described by appliance type, together with capital and running costs of gas and electric options, and some information on the characteristics of each technology and carbon emission reductions. Information about the social, cultural and institutional context in which fuel and efficiency choices are made is presented in Chapter 4.

Efficiency improvements
In order to assess improvements in efficiency, only those technical advances necessary to reach higher efficiency that pay back to the consumer are utilised. More precisely, the economic and technical feasible potential (ETP) is the level of energy efficiency that is economically justified to the consumer over the lifetime of an appliance; any additional purchase cost is paid back through energy savings. The ETP level is based on proven technology, average usage patterns, current EU electricity, water and equipment prices, with average market mark-ups and an 8% discount rate. The ETP level is equivalent to the least life cycle cost (see Glossary) and is applied to both gas and electric LAWH.

Fuel switching
Both the extent of the natural gas network, and the economic considerations of the consumer switching fuels, determine the fuel switching potential. For the UK, the Netherlands and Portugal, the potential quantified is that of switching from electricity to natural gas. Some fuel switching is already accounted for in the Reference Case, this is quite large in the case of water heating and cooking in Portugal, where many households will switch from bottled LPG to piped natural gas in the next few years given the planned network expansion and marketing initiatives.

'Lost' space heating
Some of the heat emitted by inefficient LAWH is useful space heating. Thus, if LAWH become more energy efficient, incidental heat gains will decrease, and increased demand for space heating will result. Evans and Herring (1989) estimate annual average useful incidental gains due to LAWH in a "typical British dwelling" at around 20% of space heating load. For a single person household, Boardman (1991) estimates a 7% gain. Assuming a figure somewhere between these two estimates - say 12% - and a 30% improvement in the efficiency of LAWH services then it might be expected that 4% less useful space heat would be provided by incidental gains. However, given:
- uncertainties over the assumptions used to calculate these estimates;
- the relative smallness of the figure;
- that predominantly electrically generated space heat is being displaced by predominantly more carbon efficient gas generated space heat;
- that the efficient water heating systems described later will mostly (in the UK and NL) be part of central heating systems - i.e. that space heat is also being produced more efficiently;
- that in warmer climates reduced heat gains from LAWH would also mean a reduced demand for space cooling;

the reduction of incidental heating gains are treated as second order and not included explicitly in the analysis.

3.1 MORE EFFICIENT ELECTRIC LAWH

3.1.1 Overview of savings

In order to calculate the potential savings from greater efficiency based on ETP technologies, a theoretical scenario (ETP2005) has been created. For the ETP2005 projection, the average efficiency of new appliances increases from 2000 to 2005, so that by 2005 the average efficiency of all new appliances sold is assumed to be at the ETP level. A five-year period was chosen because it should be technically feasible to achieve ETP energy consumption levels within this time scale.

Potentially, there are very large emission reductions to be obtained from the introduction of more efficient electric equipment, especially the sales of more compact fluorescent lighting (CFLs) and more efficient refrigeration appliances in all three countries. Significant reductions in energy are also available from the introduction of low power consumer electronics, especially in standby mode (Table 3.1). The potential reductions in energy and emissions are shown to the year 2020, in comparison to the Reference Case in 2020, to see the full reductions as the new equipment filters through the stock of appliances in households.

Table 3.1: Energy and carbon savings from electric efficiency, RC – ETP2005, in 2020

	UK			NL			PO		
	TWh	**MtC**	**%RC**	**TWh**	**MtC**	**%RC**	**TWh**	**MtC**	**%RC**
Cold	9.83	1.18	7.5	2.24	0.28	6.6	1.6	0.2	11.9
Consumer electronics	8.63	1.04	6.6	2.85	0.35	8.4	1.1	0.1	7.9
Cooking	2.25	0.27	1.7	0.22	0.03	0.7	0.1	0.0	0.7
Lighting	14.21	1.71	10.8	2.99	0.37	8.8	1.3	0.2	9.8
Wet	2.09	0.25	1.6	0.90	0.11	2.6	0.3	0.0	2.3
WH elec. (cylinder)	1.67	0.20	1.3	0.20	0.02	0.6	0.2	0.0	1.6
TOTAL	**38.69**	**4.65**	29.5	**9.40**	**1.15**	27.6	**4.63**	**0.63**	34.2

It is important to note that ETP2005 is not a policy scenario. In Chapter 6 a policy scenario, Kyoto+, will be described in which policies to achieve the quickest, realistic introduction of ETP are presented. This period of introduction is usually longer than the five years assumed in ETP2005 because more time is needed for production of efficient appliances to reach the required capacity. The ETP2005 projections, however, usually provide a lower boundary for the energy consumption, which may be achieved by improvements in appliance efficiency. Nevertheless, this does not represent the ultimate savings possible, as other actions such as behavioural change could contribute further savings, as could technologies that are more efficient than ETP level, though not yet considered cost-effective to the consumer.

3.1.2 ETP compared with current appliances

The ETP levels are generally based on data from EU-wide studies. For this reason the ETP technology is the same for all three countries. The gap between the current best on the market and the ETP level varies significantly between appliances (Table 3.2). For cold appliances, considerable technical advances will be required to meet the ETP level, whereas for washing machines the ETP technology is already available on the market. Further information for appliances and their potential for efficiency improvements ETP is given in Appendix F.

Table 3.2: Average, best and ETP energy/power demand levels for electric LA

		Av. New UK	RC	Best in EU*	EU av. ETP	Units
		1998	2020	1999	2020	
Cold						
	Chest freezers	409	278	195	92	kWh/yr
	Fridge-freezers	584	416	300	118	kWh/yr
	Refrigerators	239	171	144	42	kWh/yr
	Upright freezers	403	292	195	88	kWh/yr
Consumer electronics						
	Satellite RD on	16	30		21	Watt
	Satellite RD st	16	9		1	Watt
	TV-on mode	69	80		56	Watt
	TV standby	4.8	2.2	0.1	0.5	Watt
	VCR-on	22.1	20.0		32.8	Watt
	VCR-standby	5.9	1.9	1.0	1.0	Watt
Cooking						
	Oven-e	1.00	1.00	0.7	0.73	kWh empty test new
	Hob-e	0.72	0.72		0.504	kWh/use new
	Kettle	0.11	0.11		0.088	kWh/use new
Lighting	all lighting	715	841		336	kWh/hh stock
Wet						
	Washing machine	1.21	1.04	0.9	0.96	kWh/cycle
	Tumble dryer	3.48	3.12	1.75	2.60	kWh/cycle
	Dishwasher	1.46	1.35	1.1	1.10	kWh/load

* For cold appliances, EU best values are for appliances similar in size to UK average new, frost-free

3.1.3 ETP technologies

The following is a very brief summary of the technological improvements that may be required in order for appliances to reach the ETP level. Some of this information has been presented in more detail previously (DECADE, 1997a).

Cold Appliances

The ETP level identified for cold appliances is equivalent to an efficiency index (EI, see Glossary) of around 0.2 (Waide and Herring, 1993). One appliance company, AEG, has already announced that they can reach this level of efficiency on some of their products, although no cold appliances this efficient are yet in production. The most efficient cold appliance on show at the major appliance trade show in 1999, Domotechnica, had an efficiency index of 0.38. Further, a two-door fridge-freezer (from Electrolux/AEG) with an EI rating of 0.36 was presented at the Confortec fair in Paris, February 2000 (www.energy-plus.org). These figures compare with the current maximum efficiency for A-rated cold appliances with an EI index of 0.55. The technology currently envisaged to reach the ETP level is vacuum panel insulation (a vacuum is a better insulation material than foam – prototypes consist of two plastic sheets, sealed around the edges, vacuum-packed with gel or glass beads). Other technological developments, such as super efficient compressors, could also help reach this efficiency level.

Consumer electronics

Most of the potential energy saving in the consumer electronics sector comes from more efficient television screens. Television screens are assumed to be 30% more efficient in the ETP2005 scenario (E-Source, 1996). The majority of energy consumption for VCRs is in the standby mode. Given its small energy consumption, there is no necessity to have policy for the VCR on-mode. Many consumer electronics have standby losses from their 'normal' use. Through careful design, standby power demand of 1W is achievable in audio-visual equipment: the additional purchase cost is cost-effective to the consumer.

Many devices have transformers or separate power supply units – these too have the potential for very low power demand when in standby mode. The ETP level for these in this study is 0.5W. A code of conduct under discussion at the moment would set this as the desired standard within a few years (Brussels, 1999a). As this has not yet been concluded it does not form part of the Reference Case in this study.

The expected, almost universal ownership of receiver-decoders (RDs, see 2.2.2) or set top boxes indicate a large potential increase in consumption, especially in their standby mode. At present they have power demands of approximately 20W in standby, though this is expected to reduce to 9W in 2003/2004 as a result of an EU code of conduct negotiated during 1999 (Brussels, 1999b). After 2004 it is expected that additional services are added to these RDs, which may increase standby power demand. It is assumed in the ETP2005 scenario that the standby level is 1W by 2005.

Developments are possible that will combine services, which are at present provided by separate pieces of equipment, for instance the TV and the computer. The effect of these has not been modelled.

Cooking

The ETP level for electric ovens is based on the results of the recently completed EU Ovens Study (Kasanen, 2000). The key improvement required to achieve greater efficiency is improved insulation. For hobs, ETP is based on induction hob technology, currently the most efficient electric hob available. The standby power consumption of microwaves is reduced to 1W, with no improvements in on mode efficiency as no technical potential has been identified.

Lighting

It is not economically or technically feasible for CFLs to replace fluorescent strips or halogens. Therefore, the ETP calculation is based on replacing all incandescent bulbs used over a certain number of hours a year with CFLs (Table 3.3). To determine the replacement threshold, a 12-year pay back period for CFLs was assumed to be reasonable. A different threshold for replacement was calculated for 40W, 60W and 100W bulbs since the economics change at each power level.

Table 3.3 Lighting ETP: criteria for replacement of incandescent bulbs with CFLs

Incandescent	*Replaced by CFL*	*Pay back period (years)*	*Minimum usage per year for replacement (hours)*	*Replaced (%)*
40 W	10 W	12	150	80
60 W	14 W	12	100	.85
100 W	25 W	12	75	85

Source: DECADE (1997b) based on Electricity Association data

To access the ETP level by 2005 would require a huge increase in sales of CFLs: from 2% of light bulb sales in 1997, to over 85% in 2005. Obviously, this is not feasible from the point of view of production in the short term and in the longer-term bulb sales would drastically decrease due to the longer life of CFLs. In reality, ETP levels of CFL ownership would have to be introduced over a longer time scale, with mechanisms in place to provide security for the manufacturers. Also, CFLs are not suitable for all fittings; at present approximately 50% of all UK fittings can take a CFL (DELight, 1998). Improved CFLs and improved fittings are needed if the ETP level is to be reached.

Water heating

The ETP for electric stored water heating is based on minimising standing losses, through improved insulation (DESWH, 1998). The efficiency of the water-heating element is not an issue: 100% of the heat is used to heat the water.

Wet appliances

The ETP levels for all the wet appliances are those that were identified in an earlier EU study (GEA, 1995b). Washing machines and dishwashers that achieve the ETP technology level are already on the market – although they are not yet necessarily economically viable for the consumer. Nevertheless, this raises the question of whether further technical advances, not anticipated by GEA in 1995, might be possible. For instance, a heat-pump tumble dryer, which is far more efficient than the ETP (Table 3.2), is now available. Although the product (produced by AEG) is considerably more expensive than others on the market, mass manufacture would reduce the cost. The A-rated heat-pump tumble dryer has not been included in the ETP scenario - the current and expected future costs compared with its energy savings have not been determined.

3.2   MORE EFFICIENT GAS APPLIANCES AND WATER HEATING

Since gas has a lower carbon content than electricity in the three countries, the potential carbon savings are not as large as for efficiency improvements in electric appliances. Also, the potential for efficiency savings from gas appliances and water heating are less striking than those for some of the electrical LAWH – there are fewer large advances in technology to be made. With more efficient gas-fired water heating, the challenge is in increasing the market share of the most efficient rather than developing more advanced technologies.

3.2.1   Overview of savings

The only ETP savings that have been identified are those for water heating, the total savings from which are shown below (Table 3.4). Improvements to gas ovens are not justified at today's low price of gas. Since there are very few gas tumble dryers, improvements in the efficiency of this appliance was not considered. The table gives the energy and carbon savings in the year 2020 when the ETP2005 scenario is compared to the Reference Case, for gas water heating only: these carbon reductions are less than 2% in each country.

Table 3.4: Energy and carbon savings from gas efficiency, RC – ETP2005 in 2020

	UK			NL			PO		
	TWh	MtC	% RC	TWh	MtC	% RC	TWh	MtC	% RC
Gas WH (boiler)	4.56	0.24	1.5	0.59	0.03	0.7	0.52	0.03	1.7

3.2.2   ETP technologies

An EU study on domestic ovens has recently established consumption figures for gas-fired ovens under the new draft 'brick test' testing procedure. Due to the low cost of gas, design options to improve an EU reference case gas oven are not cost-effective for the consumer: the lower running cost would not repay the higher purchase price. Thus the ETP level is the same as the reference case level (Table 3.5). Nevertheless, there is still a range of efficiencies on the market, with the most efficient consuming 25% less gas than the average consumption of ovens on the market.

Table 3.5: Average, best and ETP levels for gas ovens and boilers

	Av. New UK	Best in EU	ETP level	Units
Oven	1.5	1.14	1.5	kWh
Boiler	75	92	90.5	% seasonal efficiency

Source: Ovens - Kasanen (1999)

Figures for hobs and tumble dryers are not included in this table as there is no evidence to indicate that cost-effective efficiency savings can be made for these appliances, the ETP level is assumed to be identical to the reference case. Due to the nature of gas hobs, they are already very efficient at combustion.

Condensing boilers are considered the most cost-effective types of boiler in this study. However, for the ETP2005 scenario, only 95% of new sales are assumed to be condensing boilers by 2005. This is because condensing boilers produce a slightly acidic plume of water vapour and require the installation of a small drain to remove the condensate. These characteristics may make their installation inappropriate in some cases, for instance, where houses are closely situated so that the plume could create a nuisance to neighbours. Equally, the arrangement of drains and structure of the building fabric may make installation of the condensate drain difficult. Both problems can theoretically be tackled with the outlay of sufficient expense and effort; however, there is clearly a threshold where further expense becomes prohibitive. The best estimate of the proportion of households where this is the case is 5% (Young, 2000), hence the 95% figure used.

Analysis of typical boilers on the UK market, both conventional and condensing, shows an average price difference of £250 (375 Euros) between the two for storage systems (based on data from 1999 Plumbcentre Catalogue and www.sedbuk.com). Given a conventional efficiency of 81% and condensing efficiency of 89% and typical UK usage patterns for CSWH, the additional purchase price of a condensing boiler will pay back to the consumer within 5 years (simple payback). This does not include any additional installation charge for a condensing boiler, nevertheless it clearly demonstrates that condensing boilers for storage systems meet the ETP criteria even in the UK, where they are still a niche product. In addition, one UK manufacturer is now supplying condensing boilers at the same price as conventional models.

The wasted heat from storage losses in the cylinder and from pipe runs has not been included in the consumption nor the savings. Where cylinders are used, in countries like the UK, higher levels of insulation are cost-effective. Better education of installers will result in shorter pipe runs – see Chapter 4. In all cases, the data are poor and will be improved by the new EU Water Heating Study.

3.3   FUEL SWITCHING – ELECTRICITY TO GAS

By switching from electricity to gas, the delivered energy will increase, since gas appliances are less efficient when viewed in terms of delivered energy. However, if the carbon intensity of electricity is significantly higher than gas, then there will be a reduction in overall carbon emissions. In the UK, NL and PO gas-fired appliances emit less carbon than their average electric counterpart.

Infrastructure acts as a context for making certain fuel or technology choices. Evidently, water and space heating system choices are constrained by the availability of gas. Also, for safety reasons, there are more restrictions on the location of gas than of equivalent electrical appliances. This may pose a barrier to the greater adoption of gas appliances. For example, in Northern Ireland gas dryers may not be located in either garages or bathrooms, whereas in the remainder of the UK, gas-using equipment may be located in garages. In the Netherlands, gas tumble dryers may not be installed in garages, but they are now permitted in bathrooms. In Portugal, regulations governing the installation of natural gas water heaters are stricter than those for LPG appliances, so that people changing fuels may have to change the location of their water heater as well as the burner nozzles. However, the effects seem likely to be fairly marginal.

3.3.1   Overview of savings

The estimated energy and carbon reductions from expansion of the gas network and consumers switching to gas, where economically justified and technically feasible to do so, are presented in Table 3.6. These savings have been explored via the FS-OP (fuel-switching ownership potential) scenario. The detailed assumptions underlying this scenario are described in the following sections.

Table 3.6: Delivered energy and carbon reductions from fuel switching, RC – FS-OP in 2020

	UK			NL			PO		
	TWh	MtC	%	TWh	MtC	%	TWh	MtC	%
Cooking	-1.81	0.19	1.2	-0.13	0.02	0.4	0.05	0.01	0.5
Tumble dryers	-0.55	0.12	0.8	-0.14	0.07	1.7	-0.07	0.02	0.9
Water heating	-1.26	0.33	2.1	-0.61	0.13	3.1	0.24	0.11	5.9
TOTAL	-3.62	0.64	4.1	-0.88	0.22	5.2	0.22	0.13	7.3

The table gives the changes in delivered energy and carbon emissions as a result of fuel-switching, by comparing the 2020 Reference Case with the effect of changing ownership patterns. There is no additional change to technology or usage patterns. In all three countries, delivered energy consumption increases (more gas) though carbon emissions drop between 4% and 7%. Additional effects on space heating would be substantial but have not been quantified.

The opportunities for shifting to natural gas by Portuguese domestic consumers will mainly occur in the water heating and cooking sectors, with natural gas taking some market share from electricity. All of the switch from LPG to natural gas is already accounted for in the Reference Case. With the introduction of natural gas, central heating is also expected to become more widespread.

There is still a significant amount of water heating carried out by electric resistant heating. In the NL and PO this is by individual domestic electrically stored water heaters and in the UK by the intermittent use of immersion heaters connected to the storage tank. The largest potential savings from fuel switching comes from switching this type of water heating to gas-fired.

In the Netherlands where most hobs are fuelled by gas and the oven is not used frequently, only small carbon reductions are possible through additional gas hobs and ovens. By converting to gas-fired tumble dryers significant carbon reductions can be made in both the UK and the Netherlands, and relatively less in Portugal where ownership levels are not as high.

3.3.2 Expansion of the gas network
Reference case assumptions are based on a combination of information from gas utilities, and knowledge of past rates of network expansion (Table 3.7). Only a slight expansion of the Netherlands' domestic network is envisaged in both the RC and FS-OP scenarios. The figures for both RC and FS-OP by 2020 for the UK and Portugal are discussed in some detail below.

Table 3.7: Percentage of households connected to the gas network

	1998	RC, 2020	FS-OP, 2020
UK	81	85	90
NL	96	97	97
PO	4	30	41

UK
The UK has no national targets or publicly available industry projections for expansion of the gas network. At present, 81% of households in the UK have a supply of gas in the home. The FS-OP assumes that a further 9% of households could be brought into the gas network by 2020. This is through a combination of extending the network geographically, to new areas, and of joining more households to the network in areas where gas is present, but they are not connected. An aim of 90% of households on gas is based on the census definition, which identifies 10% of the population as rural (Key Statistics, 1991). The population density in rural areas is less than one hundredth of that in urban areas making the economics of installing a gas network much less favourable.

The number of customers in Great Britain has increased by an average of 1.5% per year between 1992 and 1996, and the number of projected connections for 1997 and 1998 were in the region of 255,000 per year (BG, 1998). According to Ofgem (pers. comm., 2000) there are expected to be 125,000 connections to new housing and 90,000 connections or re-connections in 2000. The requirement to extend the gas network by 10% by 2020 is equivalent to 120,000 additional connections per annum, which is slower than rates recently achieved. This conservative rate has been taken to ensure that it is feasible, as some commentators consider that the liberalisation of domestic energy markets may act as a barrier to expansion of the gas network (Stern, pers. comm., 1999).

Natural gas has only recently been introduced to Northern Ireland. When domestic supply of natural gas started in 1997, approximately 3,000 households signed up for connection by the end of that year. The number of households having signed increased to 4,500 by April 1998. These figures were lower than the 6,000 households per year originally envisaged by Phoenix Natural Gas, the distribution company.

Indeed, the number of households actually connected by June 1998 was a mere 400. This was despite a very competitive fuel price and large subsidies for the introduction of gas into the area. It is thought that uptake has been low because those people who are most likely to switch fuels, the solid fuel users, are also the poorest and generally living in rented accommodation. Thus they have neither the capital nor the security of tenure to justify investing in a new heating system to take advantage of natural gas. However, partly due to the more-than doubling of heating oil prices (from £85 at the end of 1998 to £190 at the beginning of 2000 for a standard 900L delivery), customers are currently being connected at a rate of 350 per week, and 25,000 domestic customers are signed up (www.phoenix-natural-gas.com). For a limited period, Phoenix Natural Gas is offering free connection (worth £400) in the network area, and one year's half-price gas. For more detail on the introduction of natural gas to Northern Ireland, see Appendix N.

Portugal
Portugal has a policy goal of reducing its dependence on oil; the expansion of a natural gas network is encouraged. By the end of 1998 the four regional supply companies anticipated a network supplying 74,000 domestic consumers (2.4% of householders). It is anticipated that by 2010 the network will have extended to 568,000 domestic consumers (13% of the predicted population at that time). The north of Portugal does not have a tradition of using LPG. Therefore consumers in the north are unfamiliar with the use of gas. Consequently, they have a greater concern about the safety of natural gas than consumers from other regions. In order to overcome this consumer resistance, Portgás, the company operating in the north, is operating a more vigorous marketing campaign than other regional companies. Portgás has also been giving away free gas water heaters with gas installation, to encourage consumers to sign up.

Under the reference case it is assumed that 30% of Portuguese households will have been connected to the gas network by 2020. However, it would be economic for many more to do so, the extent to which the network could expand more quickly is the key question. There have been a number of problems which have slowed the expansion of the network to date, including: lack of trained personnel, inadequate gas networks in new housing (which were built to allow easy connection to natural gas), and a poor standard of workmanship leading to customer dissatisfaction. For more details on the introduction of natural gas to Portugal see Appendix R (whole Europe).

In the FS-OP scenario, the network is assumed to expand so that 41% of domestic consumers have access to natural gas, mainly for water heating.

3.3.3 Change in ownership
The change in ownership which is modelled under the FS-OP scenario is as a result of assumptions about extension of the gas network in the UK and Portugal (Table 3.8), in addition to switching to gas appliances and water heating by households on the existing network.

Table 3.8: Ownership of gas and electric appliances, RC and FS-OP

Country		1998		RC, 2020		FS-OP, 2020	
		Gas	Electric	Gas	Electric	Gas	Electric
UK	Hob	54	46	57	43	90	10
	Oven	41	57	31	69	73	27
	Tumble dryer	0.3	35	0.5	35	26.5	9
	Water heating (all)	78	63	85	57	90	10
NL	Hob	85	15	85	15	97	3
	Oven	20	64	20	56	62	14
	Tumble dryer	0	56	0	62	42	20
	Water heating (all)	93	24	93	24	107	10
PO	Hob	85	12	85	12	91	6
	Oven	85	12	85	12	91	6
	Tumble dryer	0	8	0	25	17	8
	Water heating (all)	68	16	72	16	84	4

UK

For the UK it is assumed that people newly connected to the gas network would automatically choose gas for their space and water heating fuel, as this is by far the most popular fuel for these services, particularly amongst owner-occupiers. Where other systems are installed, it is usually because there is no gas main nearby. This is despite some health and safety concerns - particularly the generation of incomplete combustion products, mainly carbon monoxide. Far more people die every year in the UK from 'burnt gas poisoning' than from gas explosions (BG, 1998), which has led to a tightening of regulations relating to gas appliances. Private landlords must now have an annual check of their gas appliances by a registered installer. Subsequently, large numbers of landlords have removed gas room heating and replaced it with electric fires. However, amongst owner-occupiers safety concerns do not seem to have affected the popularity of gas as a heating fuel.

In the FS-OP scenario, it is assumed that 90% of all new hobs, ovens and tumble dryers would be gas-fired, and that the ownership levels listed above could be reached by 2020. Electric immersion heaters are not used as summer/top-up usage and are only a main source of water heating in the 10% of homes beyond the gas network.

NL

Under this scenario all households that are connected to the gas network will purchase a gas hob when the time comes to purchase a new or replacement hob. However, since ovens are used infrequently, it is not cost-effective for the households to choose gas if they were going to purchase an electric oven. Thus, there is no economic fuel switching potential for Dutch ovens. Since gas is much more cost-effective than electric for water heating, only 3% will have domestic electric stored water heating under the FS-OP scenario as main sources of water heating. Secondary electric water heating will still be present.

PO

Switching to natural gas in Portugal is occurring as the network expands. For those on LPG, the switch requires only a simple adjustment of the burner, but saves 17% of the carbon immediately. For those with electricity, the savings are greater, but the household is faced with the cost of replacing the equipment as well. The Portuguese Demand Side Management (DSM, Appendix P) project established, based on a sample of 25 houses who had already converted to natural gas:

For water heating:
- 5 switched from LPG to natural gas
- 2 changed from electricity to integrated space and water heating, gas boiler
- 18 changed from electricity to instantaneous gas water heating.

For cooking:
- 2 households had all electric cooking and did not change
- 23 households with all gas or mixed cooking, switched the LPD to natural gas

The maximum savings (for the households that changed from electricity to natural gas for both water heating and cooking) were:
- nearly 2 euros/day in running costs
- reduced carbon emissions of 0.74 kgC a day.

Under the FS-OP scenario electric hobs and ovens are converted to natural gas, where the infrastructure will allow until 91% are connected to natural gas or LPG. DESWHs are reduced from 16 to 4% under this scenario and these households each save 191 kgC annually, and an extra 80 kgC where cooking was by electricity.

For all three countries, hypothetically under the FS-OP scenario, the ownership of gas tumble dryers will gradually replace that of electric ones where the household is connected to the gas network.

3.3.4 Carbon savings per appliance type

Switching from an average (Reference Case) electric appliance to a more efficient one or to a gas-fired one can reduce carbon emissions. Table 3.9 shows the estimated carbon reductions, per use, for four different appliances. In this table, the carbon dioxide conversion factors used are 0.11 and 0.05 kgC per delivered kWh for electricity and gas respectively, the average across Europe in 1995.

Table 3.9: Carbon reductions due to fuel switching from electricity to natural gas

			TD	Oven	Hob	Water heat
Electric, RC	kWh/use		3.50	1.20	0.72	1.00
	kgC		0.38	0.13	0.08	0.11
Electric, ETP	kWh/use		2.60	0.87	0.50	1.00
	kgC		0.29	0.10	0.06	0.11
Electric, best	kWh/use		1.75	0.70	0.50	1.00
	kgC		0.19	0.08	0.06	0.11
Gas-fired, RC	kWh/use	Gas	3.86	1.52	1.00	1.18
		Elec[*]	0.43			
	kgC		0.25	0.08	0.05	0.06

[*] electric motor and controls

In all cases the reference case gas appliance emits less carbon than the equivalent RC electric appliance. However, the difference is reduced if the gas appliances are compared to efficient ETP electric appliances (apart from water heating, where it is difficult to improve the efficiency without using heat pumps). In the case of heat-pump tumble dryers (best electric tumble dryer), the emissions can even be less than the gas tumble dryer, since the gas tumble dryer still needs electricity to drive the motor. Thus, switching to gas will reduce emissions, though the difference is less when compared to very efficient electric appliances.

3.3.5 Costs of fuel switching

There can be additional costs associated with installing gas appliances, which do not apply to their electrical equivalents.

Gas installation costs can be broken down into three categories:
- to the house
- from the door into the home
- connection to the existing network within the home

The cost of connecting houses to the gas network should not be included in the costs attributed to switching to gas appliances, but could be borne by the energy companies in order to persuade customers to sign up. The cost of installing gas within a home would normally be associated with the installation of space and water heating; it will last longer than just one appliance. Thus it is very doubtful that this cost should be added to the cost of choosing a gas appliance. The only component of these costs considered for the appliances below (Table 3.10) is the connection to the existing network within the home.

These data show that it is already economic to the individual consumer to choose gas over electricity, despite the higher purchase price and installation costs in some cases. Consumer decision-making regarding fuel switching, particularly non-economic aspects, is discussed in more depth in Chapter 4.

Table 3.10: Comparison of costs of gas and electric tumble dryers and cookers, UK, 1998

	Tumble dryer			Cooker (hob + oven)	
	Electric venting	Electric condensing	Gas	Electric	Gas
Purchase price (sales weighted average in the UK, 1998)	£180	£305	£250	£461	£492
Installation cost (estimates)	0	0	£75	£30	£50
Running cost (per year)	£26	£26	£11	£35	£14
Simple pay back to consumer – purchasing gas instead of electric (years)			(venting) 10 (condensing) 1.4		0.5

Sources: Prices – analysis of market research data; usage – DECADE model

The costs of electric and gas water heating cannot be compared in the same way for the UK, primarily because gas water heating is provided via a combined space and water heating system. In addition, consumer reasons for choice of fuels for space heating is not primarily based on economics. Gas CSWH is simply more convenient and adds to the value of a property in a way that electric space and water heating does not.

3.4   TOTAL CARBON SAVINGS FROM FUEL SWITCHING AND EFFICIENCY

If consumers were to purchase the most efficient appliances, and switch to gas where appropriate, there would be a large reduction in carbon emissions. The result of this hypothetical situation, the FS-ETP scenario, is shown in Figure 3.1.

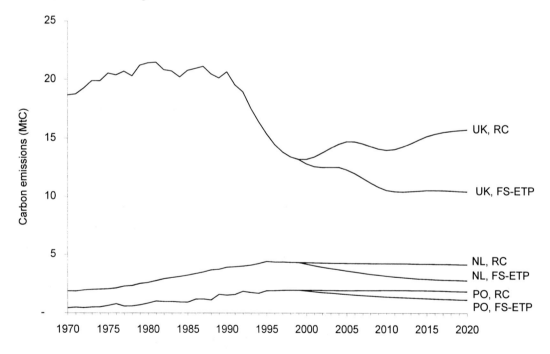

Figure 3.1: Carbon emissions under the RC and FS-ETP scenarios, 1970-2020

3.4.1   Potential carbon savings

Under the FS-ETP scenario, by 2010 the UK could potentially reduce emissions by over 3MtC from the Reference Case, without any loss of service to the consumer (Table 3.11). The savings would increase to over 5MtC by 2020. Similarly, for the Netherlands and Portugal potential emission reductions are of the order of 1.1 and 0.6MtC respectively by the year 2010. These carbon reductions combine both the ETP for gas and electric and the fuel switching ownership potential. The results are not cumulative – the choice is between buying a more efficient electric appliance or a gas appliance.

Table 3.11: Potential carbon reductions in 2010 and 2020, compared to RC

	UK		NL		PO	
	MtC	% of RC	MtC	% of RC	MtC	% of RC
RC - FS-ETP, 2010	3.44	24.6	1.06	25.0	0.57	29.2
RC - FS-ETP, 2020	5.32	33.7	1.37	32.8	0.72	39.0
From electric efficiency, 2010*	2.97	21.2	0.90	21.2	0.42	21.9
From gas efficiency, 2010*	0.24	1.7	0.02	0.4	0.02	0.9
From fuel switching, 2010*	0.44	3.2	0.17	4.0	0.15	7.5

* Efficiency and fuel switching savings are estimated separately, and it is these figures that are presented here. Summing the individual savings to obtain a total would result in some double counting.

In all three countries, the carbon reductions from electrical appliances represent in excess of 80% of the total potential reductions available by 2020 through cost-effective improvements in electric and gas efficiency and fuel switching.

3.4.2   Allocating carbon dioxide to fuel savings

Converting electricity savings into carbon savings is more complex than obtaining current and future electricity consumption figures. This is due to the additional issue of marginal versus average kgC/kWh conversion factors. When electricity is saved, the savings will come from reduced generating fuels, depending on the composition of the electricity production system, the prices of fuels and the usage patterns of appliances.

Furthermore, a distinction can be made between:
- short-term marginal carbon emission savings – savings are made initially on electricity with the highest variable cost and ease of response. Depending on the country this is some combination of natural gas, heavy fuel oil , coal (sometimes the order is changed, eg due to low natural gas prices, time of day);
- long-term marginal carbon emission savings – if electricity savings persist over time this will lead to a smaller electricity generating capacity; long-term marginal savings may be quite different from the short-term marginal savings.

Without sophisticated models of the electricity system and electricity demand it is difficult to estimate marginal savings. For the longer term this task is even more difficult as the considerations are not purely economic, but political and strategic (eg, diversification, bans on nuclear, energy and climate policy). Nevertheless, it is reasonable to conclude that most electricity savings will lead to savings of fossil fuel generated electricity: the development of the two most important alternatives (nuclear and hydro) is constrained by other factors. However by 2010, the saving will generally be from natural gas, the fuel with the lowest specific carbon emission, than from other fossil fuels.

For comparability, the FS-ETP and FS-OP scenarios use the same carbon conversion figures as in the Reference Case thus potentially overestimating potential carbon reductions in NL and PO.

3.5   FURTHER OPTIONS FOR CARBON EMISSION REDUCTIONS

Although not included in the modelling of savings above, there are further options that could allow fuel switching to lower carbon fuels. The potential for savings from behavioural change is also described. In addition, there are further efficiency improvements that have not been included in ETP. These are described and briefly explored below. This does not include the increased use of renewable energy, which is discussed from the consumer perspective in Chapter 4.

3.5.1 Behavioural change

The FS-ETP savings potential does not include any saving from changing patterns of usage (beyond what would be expected under the Reference Case). Potential savings from behavioural change with regards to electric appliances and lighting, whilst still achieving the same standard of service, were identified in previous work (DECADE, 1997b) and will not be revisited here. The net effect could be to save up to 12% from electric lights and appliances through measures such as loading wet appliances more fully, not using standby mode on TVs, and defrosting cold appliances. Those savings being within the context of unchanged levels of service did not include options such as people choosing to hang washing outside to dry rather than using their tumble dryers. Broader lifestyle issues such as this are discussed in Chapter 6. DECADE (1997b) also showed that the time of use of an appliance would affect emissions. This is due to the changing supply mix during the day in the UK. Using off-peak electricity can result in modest carbon reductions (about 10%) and relatively substantial financial savings.

The reason this behavioural potential is not included in the scenarios is that policies to guarantee behavioural changes are few and far between. Detailed work on whether householders would be prepared to make certain behavioural changes has been undertaken in the Netherlands (Groot-Marcus and Uitenbogerd, 1999). This has shown that householders for a variety of reasons do not favour many of the theoretically possible behavioural changes, and as little as 20% of the theoretical savings may be made in real life.

Despite the difficulty in designing policy to achieve behavioural change, this still remains an element of public policy. For example, the European Commission has signed an agreement with AISE (Association Internationale de la Savonnerie, de la Détergence et des Produits d'Entretien, the European soap and detergent association) to develop improved lower temperature detergents and provide information to consumers to reduce consumers' wash temperatures - which should reduce energy consumption (AISE, 2000).

Informative bills

In Norway, domestic energy use fell by about 10% after the introduction of regular 'informative bills' which explained to customers how their energy use compared with that in previous time periods (Wilhite and Ling, 1995). The energy savings have been shown to persist over time. Informative bills therefore present a very good opportunity for consumers to save energy, although it is not certain that such large savings could be achieved in other countries or for all socio-economic groups. For instance, the size of the response to feedback information seems related to the proportion of energy costs in the household budget: Winkler and Winett (1982) found that feedback had no effect when energy costs were no more than two percent of the household budget. At 5%, feedback produced reductions of around 15%. Consequently, in the UK, it may be that feedback is particularly effective amongst poorer groups (Green *et al.*, 1998).

Summer use of combined water and space heating systems

As mentioned in Chapter 2, approximately 9% of UK households use electric immersion heaters in summer, even though they used gas central heating in winter. Persuading these households to use gas all year round would result in carbon dioxide savings (and would result in cost savings for the householders). This is likely to be a decreasing option as people tend towards installing instantaneous boilers.

3.5.2 Heat-fed wet appliances

Ecofys undertook work on heat-fed washing machines and tumble dryers, for full details see Appendix K. This type of appliance uses piped-in (externally heated) hot water, which heats water (or air) inside the machine through a heat-exchanger. This arrangement is particularly useful where there is excessive district heating, which is beginning to happen in the Netherlands due to improving levels of insulation resulting in less space heating demand, or where hot water can be produced efficiently in the home. Application of heat-fed washing machines and tumble dryers is a promising fuel-switching option for households. It increases heat demand in district heating networks, it saves primary energy and it can save costs. In this way, it can benefit utilities, the environment and consumers at the same time.

Table 3.12: Laboratory measured savings and costs for various wet appliances

	Primary energy consumption (MJ$_{prim}$/cycle)	Primary energy savings (%)	Additional cost (Euros/ appliance)	Annual savings (Euros/ appliance)	Payback time (years)
Washing machine					
Conventional	8.1				
Heat-fed, district heating	3.5	56	111	27	4.1
Heat-fed, central heating	5.5	32	157	32	4.9
Heat-fed, central+solar	4.5	44	157	35	4.4
Hot-fill	5.5	32	66	25	2.7
Tumble dryer					
Conventional condensing	25.6				
Heat-fed, district heating	12.0	53	211	56	3.7
Heat-fed, central heating	18.5	28	211	69	3.0
Heat-fed, central + solar	15.2	41	211	77	2.7
Heat pump	12.9	50	454	63	7.2
Gas-fired	14.8	39	238	79	3.0

Source: See Appendix K

Prototype heat-fed washing machines and tumble dryers were previously developed, where utilities participated by buying prototype heat-fed machines. Thirteen households were selected for placement of the machines to conduct one-year field-tests. The aim of the field trial was to establish the technical performance in practice, and to examine how users would judge the appliance. In eleven of the thirteen participating households, the heat-fed appliance was connected to a district-heating network. In one household the machines were connected to the central heating system. In another household the machines were connected to a central heating system that incorporated a solar domestic hot water system.

Measured savings
The washing machines functioned well during the field trials. Averaged over all households, a yearly primary energy saving of 43% was achieved when connect to district heating. The tumble dryer also worked well *in situ*, where the yearly primary energy savings amounted to 52%. The heat-fed appliances has shown to perform as well when connected to central heating systems (rather than to district heating systems). However, the primary energy savings are lower. From the field test data, savings of 18 and 23%, respectively, were calculated for the washing machine and the tumble dryer.

User feedback
Householders were very content with the washing machine. Evaluation of the dryer varied significantly from one household to another. Noise appears to be the biggest factor, causing mixed feelings about the dryer. Some households found the drying cycles took too long. Some households thought the dryer functioned better than their previous machine, whereas others thought its drying performance was inferior. Some of these issues could be addressed in future models.

Conclusions and further developments
The field-tests showed that there are no technical barriers for further development and large-scale application of the heat-fed apparatus. In addition, users have indicated their satisfaction in using the heat-fed appliance. A comparison of the heat-fed concept with other energy saving concepts (hot-fill washing machines, gas-fired dryers, heat-pump dryers) show that the heat-fed appliance combine large energy savings with moderate cost, and therefore are promising options for fuel switching. A brief inquiry also showed Europe-wide interest by utilities for application of heat-fed appliances.

3.5.3 Hot-fill washing machines

Hot-fill washing machines are standard in the UK, with an estimated 90% of washing machines being attached to both the hot and cold water supply. For hot wash cycles the machine takes in hot water from the home's existing hot water system, and as this is usually gas-fired it results in lower carbon emissions than heating the water in the washing machine electrically (Table 3.12). However, in other EU countries the hot-fill washing machine is almost unknown, and indeed perceived to be undesirable. The Dutch believe that taking hot water into a washing machine would fix existing stains into clothing and would result in a poorer wash quality.

It would therefore seem that undertaking work on an intelligent hot-fill machine, which mixed water on entry such that clothes would not be exposed to higher than desired temperatures at different stages of the wash, could increase the prospects for hot-fill in other EU countries. In addition, it could ensure that gas-heated hot water was used for the lower temperature washes (40°C and below) which are increasingly favoured by EU householders. Many UK washing machines do not use household hot water, which is normally at 60°C, for low temperature washes.

3.5.4 Heat pump water heaters

A heat pump converts unused energy into usable heat. Heat pumps have been developed for space, water and for combined space and water heating. By 1998 in the Netherlands, 3,732 water heaters and 795 combination systems had been installed. The technology of heat pumps is still improving and costs are decreasing. The energy savings that can be expected are very much dependent on the design and use of the system, but can be around 60% compared with either gas or electric systems.

The use of heat pump water heaters is currently almost unknown in the UK. Solar-assisted heat pumps have been made and sold in Portugal for several years, but sales remain low.

3.5.5 Solar water heating

Solar water heating systems use the sun to heat either water or a heat-transfer fluid in collectors generally mounted on a roof. The heated water is then stored in a tank similar to a conventional gas or electric water tank. Solar water heaters are made up of collectors, storage tanks, and, depending on the system, electric pumps. Solar water heaters can operate in any climate. Performance varies depending, in part, on how much solar energy is available at the site, but also on how cold the water coming into the system is. In all European climates, a conventional backup system is also required. For successful installation, there must be enough room on the roof or the ground for a properly sized collector; the roof should be unshaded and either flat or tilted south. These requirements mean that solar water heating is not an option for all households.

In general, simpler, less expensive systems work well in warmer climates. An effective solar water heating system in Northern Europe needs to be more complex, and thus more expensive, making the economics of purchase less favourable. The penetration of solar water heating in different European countries is not simply linked to climate and the cost of alternative fuels: where there is no strong government programme, patterns of adoption are strongly linked to consumer environmental awareness (ESIF, 1995).

The market for solar water heating in the UK is currently small. There are some local initiatives to encourage installation of solar water heating, but no national programme. An estimated 43GWh energy from approximately 30,000 systems was supplied for domestic water heating by solar water heating in 1998 (DUKES, 1999). The payback on solar water heating varies from four years (DIY installation replacing electric water heating system) to 30 years (durable system replacing gas, in a two-person household). The cost effectiveness is increased considerably when the solar water heating is installed during the construction stage, rather than retrofitted. The financial costs are also distorted by the fiscal system. VAT is charged at 17.5% on the solar water heating system, whilst the fuel saved is taxed at 5% (in the UK).

The Netherlands has a strong existing programme for promoting solar water heating. The programme is based on a long-term agreement between the Ministry of Economic Affairs, Novem - the Dutch energy agency, energy companies, and manufacturers of solar water heating systems. The agreement guarantees price reductions for solar thermal systems through subsidies from both central government and the energy companies. Firms can also claim tax allowances if they invest in solar thermal systems. The Dutch have also established an Energy Performance Standard for new build. As this is further tightened in 2000 it is expected that solar water heaters will begin to be offered as standard by housing developers. It is estimated that there were 15,100 installed systems at the end of 1996 (Minez, 1997). As a result of the schemes, between 8-10,000 new systems have been installed each year since then. The goals of a recent covenant were to stimulate market development and application of solar water heaters, develop an independent market able to grow to 400,000 cumulatively installed systems in 2010, and develop policy instruments to stimulate application in existing buildings.

Although Portugal has very favourable conditions for the use of solar water heating, the uptake is low (less than 3%). Greece, with similar weather conditions, has at least ten times more solar water heating.

3.5.6 Combined heat and power
Combined heat and power (CHP) is the simultaneous generation of usable heat and power (usually electricity) in a single process. CHP typically achieves a 25 to 35% reduction in primary energy usage compared with electricity-only generation and heat-only boilers (DUKES, 1999).

Micro CHP
Micro-co-generation systems for single domestic dwellings offer further opportunities for carbon efficient generation of heating and electricity. In the UK, several boiler manufacturers and research organisations have already built viable units that are no bigger than conventional boilers. If integrated appropriately they offer electrical load-management, as well as fuel-saving, opportunities and a mass-production market for manufacturing and utility companies to exploit. In the UK and the Netherlands, the well-established and extensive natural gas grid allows the direct replacement of micro-CHP units for conventional central heating boilers (IEE, 1999).

District heating
District heating systems (also known as co-generation or community heating) mostly utilise the 'waste' heat, released in power generation, for space heating and water heating in offices, public buildings and homes.

In the Netherlands, co-generation has been emphasised in policy and power industry plans to meet the aim of carbon dioxide-emission reduction. The official target for 2000 is an installed capacity of 8,000MW$_e$ leading to a market share for co-generation of 50%, heat generation from CHP is planned to increase from 3.3 TWh in 1990 to 7.8 TWh in 2000. Presently, annual sales are at 7.5 TWh. These policies build on a strong increase in district heating since the early 1980s. Indeed, at the beginning of 1988, district heating was installed in 31 cities. The number of connections steadily increased from 100,000 dwelling-equivalents in 1981 to about 365,000 dwelling-equivalents by the end of 1997. CHP plants now produce much of this heating. The electric power output from these has grown in the past 16 years from about 350 MW$_e$ to about 1800 MW$_e$ (ECOFYS, 2000).

In contrast to the Netherlands there is very little district heating in the UK, and most of it is independent of power generation. District heating is not significant in Portugal either.

3.6 CONCLUSIONS
There is the potential to reduce the carbon emissions by LAWH in the three countries significantly by the introduction of more efficient electric and gas-fired appliances and also through fuel switching. Realising the full ETP potential including fuel switching could reduce emissions by 3.4 MtC in UK, 1 MtC in the Netherlands and 0.6 MtC in Portugal from the level projected in 2010. By 2020 the potential for reduction would have increased to 5.3MtC in UK, 1.4MtC in the Netherlands and 0.7 MtC in Portugal from the level projected.

The largest potential carbon reductions are from the increase in the efficiency of cold appliances and increase of sales of CFLs at the expense of GLS bulbs. In addition, the early introduction of very efficient consumer electronic appliances will prevent a large increase in the electricity consumption of these appliances. The potential savings are larger for electric appliances partly due to electricity being a more carbon intensive fuel than gas.

Efficiency improvements to gas boilers do reduce gas consumption significantly though it does not provide large reductions in carbon by 2010, when compared to the potential reduction by electric appliances and lighting. This is due to several factors. By 2010, the natural rate of turnover means that much less than half of all, older and less efficient, boilers will have been replaced. Also, additional carbon reductions will arise as a result of this increased efficiency since standing and distribution losses have not been included in this analysis – only the energy required to heat the water. In addition, if the boiler is part of a combined space and water heating system, as is becoming more prevalent, much larger savings from space heating will accrue at the same time.

Heat-fed appliances will reduce carbon emissions and cost-effective where there is district heating. Attaching the heat-fed appliances to a central water heating system could also reduce emissions though the cost-effectiveness is less certain at present. Increasing the volume of production could reduce costs sufficiently to be viable when connected to a household's central water heating system

As an average across the EU, very efficient electric appliances (tumble dryers, ovens, hobs) can emit as little carbon as their gas-fired equivalents. This is not the case for water heaters unless heat-pump technologies are considered.

The potential cost-effective carbon savings are large. However, there are reasons why these potential reductions are not being realised, and may never be realised, and are considered in the following chapter.

CHAPTER 4: REAL CHOICES

This chapter explains why the potential for fuel switching and introduction of more efficient heating and appliances chosen in the policy scenarios in Chapter 6 may not be as large as the theoretical potential identified in Chapter 3. In reality, consumers have restricted incomes and fuel choices, imperfect information, face limited choices in the retail environment, have to rely on the advice of professionals and, not unreasonably, have priorities other than energy and carbon efficiency. Consumers are people - bound into complex webs of social and cultural expectations that influence what is considered desirable, acceptable and normal. This may be very different from what is, in theory, economically justified and environmentally beneficial. In addition, retailers, manufacturers, installers, energy companies, architects and others all have an influence on what ends up in the home, and their business is not based around recommending low carbon solutions.

Chapter 3 concluded that the greatest carbon reductions would most likely come from improvements in the efficiency of lighting, cold appliances and gas water heating systems. In addition there was considerable scope for fuel switching from electricity to gas. The decision-making environment for more efficient lighting is explored in detail in DeLight (1998) and so is not revisited here. Instead, discussion focuses on the specification of water-heating systems and cold appliances in the UK and two forms of fuel switching - adoption of gas tumble dryers, as opposed to electric, in the Netherlands, and the decision to buy "green electricity" in the UK. These case histories illustrate not only some of the most important carbon saving options but provide more generic lessons on aspects of the market transformation tool kit – namely design and targeting of information, subsidies, institutional change and consumer education.

4.1   THE CONTEXT OF CHOICE

Physical, institutional and social structures acts as a context for making certain fuel or technology choices. Evidently, water and space heating system choices are constrained by the physical presence of a gas main. As such, urban households are more likely than rural to have natural gas central heating. Physical infrastructure can also influence the pattern of energy demand. For example, tumble dyers are more likely to be owned in houses with no place outside to dry clothes. Similarly, the lack of space in older properties is thought to be constraining European demand for dishwashers (Appliance, 1997). In this way household infrastructure can act as a driver as well as a barrier to increased energy demand.

In addition to physical aspects of infrastructure, institutional and regulatory arrangements form a second level of context to domestic choice. For example, on a regulatory level, there are more restrictions on the location of gas than of equivalent electrical appliances. This may pose a barrier to the greater adoption of gas appliances. At an institutional level, systems of provisioning, transport, work patterns, etc., all determine what kind of appliances are appropriate and available. For example, whereas 20 years ago in the UK, freezers were generally large objects kept in the garage that could be used to store bulk quantities of foods to economise and beat the seasons, now they are smaller and have come inside the house, often as part of fridge freezers. In doing so their role has changed to one that is more suitable for storage of convenience foods – frozen pizza, etc. These changes in the appropriate choice of appliance (i.e. an upright fridge-freezer rather than chest freezer) are a direct response to changing work patterns and domestic roles, the establishment of distribution systems that can provide cheap prepared frozen foods, and so on. In addition, ownership of some appliances encourages ownership of others - suites of domestic technologies have been designed that match or complement one another. For example, the fridge-freezer's effectiveness as a convenient technique for providing fast food is assisted by the use of microwave oven, which is often used simply as a defroster rather than as a cooking device (Southerton and Shove, 1999).

Cultural norms and social expectations can be conceptually distinguished as a third level of context. Behaving in a certain way, or buying and displaying certain products that do not match the expectations of others whose opinion one values, will evidently be discouraged. For instance, an American study found that using a clothes line rather than a tumble dryer (in the heat of a Texan summer) made men appear less ambitious, more working class and even, bizarrely, more homosexual (Sadalla and Krull, 1995). As another example, current expectations of cleanliness and hygiene allied with increasing use of leisure time for sport virtually necessitate, for many households, the ownership and frequent use of a washing machine.

Whilst these levels of physical, institutional and social context are conceptually distinct, their continued existence and reproduction depend upon each other. They are levels of a mutually reinforcing system which encourages certain choices and lifestyles and imposes heavy costs otherwise. However, whilst the influence of these contexts is evidently important in decision-making about ownership of generic types of product – washing machines, water heating systems, etc., it may be thought that decision-making about the choice of whether those services are provided relatively efficiently would be more a matter for individual self reflection and judgement. This is certainly the case for some products that do not require expert skills for selection or installation - such as refrigerators. However, other categories of product, such as boilers, do require such skills. In these cases specification is once more taken out of the control of the householder and becomes subject to the wider world of social and institutional forces. The decision-making environments of a number of domestic technologies are considered below. Each illustrates varying degrees of influence of the levels of context outlined above.

4.2   WATER HEATING

4.2.1   UK water heating survey

Hot water, cooking and laundry equipment in 24 houses, with a range of fuel types and tenancies, were surveyed in early 1999. During these site visits, the most effective improvements to reduce running costs and associated carbon dioxide emissions were evaluated, giving costs and savings for each measure. The householder was then invited to comment on the proposed improvements. Half the homes surveyed used electricity for water heating. The bias towards electricity (compared with the national distribution) was deliberate, due to the significantly higher carbon dioxide savings that can be made by the substitution of other fuels for electricity. Full details can be found in Appendix M.

Technically the general standard of hot water systems found was poor. Even those using gas often had old cast iron boilers, sometimes with missing controls. Such systems have very low efficiency. Losses from long pipe runs were also surprisingly large. The kitchen hot tap draw-off varied from 1.2 to 5.0 litres before hot water arrived at the tap. This latter figure represents a considerable lack of convenience. Some households circumvented long draw-offs by other means - such as using an electric kettle. The two largest draw-offs, 5 and 4 litres, were the result of inefficient system layouts and could have been significantly shortened quite easily.

Even in this small sample, the survey found a large range of costs of hot water per person– from £16 to £140 (24 to 210 Euros) per person per year, with a slightly smaller range of carbon dioxide emissions per person per year: 221 to 924kg carbon dioxide. The household hot water costs ranged from £50 (75 Euros) to just under £400 (600 Euros) per year. However, for most surveyed, payback periods for improvements to the water heating systems were unacceptably long. Perhaps more importantly, householders seemed unconcerned about having an inefficient hot water system unless they also had a convenience problem. Such problems included: having a fuel that is perceived as being too expensive to leave 'on tap'; having to wait for hot water to be delivered to the hot tap due to long pipe runs; running out of hot water due to inadequate storage.

4.2.2   Efficient gas boilers

The network of economic and institutional relationships between all those involved in the specification of domestic heating systems in the UK (such as installers, manufacturers, developers, etc.) has developed such that the most efficient appliances, heating and control systems are generally not installed. For example, condensing boilers (the most efficient kind) constitute only 5% of new installations (Young, 2000). In the Netherlands condensing boilers (CBs) have 60% of the market share. This has been achieved using subsidies and training for installers rather than regulation. The structure of the Dutch installation industry is similar to the UK, as is the extent of the domestic gas supply network. Ostensibly, the Dutch success story in promoting this efficient technology is the model the UK should follow. The UK's Energy Savings Trust (EST) has also operated an intermittent rebate scheme for CBs since 1993.

Under these schemes CB buyers have been able to claim between £100-£200 (150-300 Euros), depending in which tranche of the scheme the claim was made. More recently, some training has been also been provided. It remains to be seen whether CBs will eventually take the same market share as in the Netherlands. Certainly, the rate of uptake in the UK is already far slower.

The purpose of this section is to analyse the relationships and orientations of the key actors in the UK heating industry so that the reasons for slower market penetration rates of innovative and energy saving technologies in the UK become apparent. The analysis is based on lengthy interviews with a number of representatives of each actor group during the summer of 1999, and two quantitative questionnaire surveys of householders undertaken for the ECI by GfK marketing in March 1998 (n = 2200) and November 1999 (n = 130). A brief characterisation of the relationships between the key actors is shown in Figure 4.1. While supporting material (presented in Appendix C) considers all these relationships in detail and gives detailed policy recommendations, discussion here will focus on householders, installers and the manufacturers.

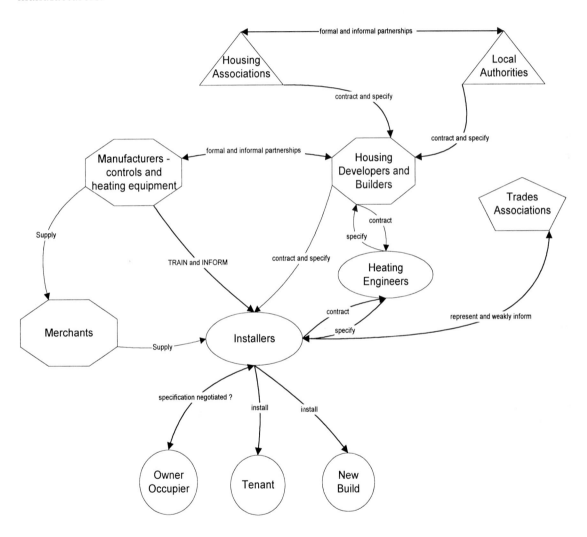

Figure 4.1: Network of actors implicated in the specification of domestic heating equipment, UK

Householders
GfK survey data suggest that owner-occupiers have three principal motivations to change their heating systems: system breakdown or development of faults (around 50-60%), home improvements, particularly kitchen refits, (around 20%) and, probably more rarely, changing household needs which require a boiler with a higher output or different qualities (6-7%). A system change prompted by concerns over the efficiency of the existing installation seems rarer - perhaps four or five percent of all installations. Many

make these assessments on moving into a new house. Evidently, this is an important trigger point where householders tend to consider the infrastructure of the dwelling and are sensitive to the possibility of spending large sums on improvements.

The installer, rather than the householder, usually specifies new heating equipment. This is despite GfK's finding that 70% of householders feel that they have time to 'gather information' before the installer is called in. Indeed, GfK reports that around three-quarters of householders *only* use information and advice provided by the installer when choosing their new system. Those that do obtain information from elsewhere actively seek it out from sources such as builders and plumbers merchants rather than gaining it through more passive means, such as TV and press advertising. This is unlikely to change: homeowners will only become interested in such information when they are in the process of considering buying a new heating system and this is a rare event in most people's lifetime. As such, the vast majority will largely ignore untargeted public awareness campaigns. Even amongst the target group (of those in the market for new heating equipment), GfK surveys found that only 20% were aware of the EST rebate on condensing boilers.

Contrary to expectations, price is the principal selection criterion for a new heating system of only 10% of respondents, and only half of householders obtain more than one quote to allow comparisons. This may be explained by the overwhelming use of installers that are recommended by others and again reflects the dependence on installer advice. It is apparent that there is a great opportunity for an enthusiastic installer to encourage the householder to invest a little more in efficient equipment.

Installers

Installers are broadly responsible for the specification of heating systems in existing housing. However, they are conservative in suggesting brands and models to householders – quoting for what they know to be reliable, are comfortable with, and that they have the tools and spares to fix if anything should go wrong. This conservatism will inevitably orientate installers away from new or innovative products. Whilst the CB is not new it remains relatively innovative and is often significantly more expensive than conventional boilers. In addition, installers perceive the CB as delivering only marginal energy savings in the domestic context and as being unreliable. Consequently, installers will not suggest condensing boilers until they feel that there is a strong demand for them. Even householders who express a clear and unprompted desire for a condensing boiler may be discouraged until installers become familiar with the technology and are satisfied that they are as reliable as conventional boilers.

This has led to a vicious circle preventing widespread penetration: installers do not suggest CBs, so householders who may have been interested are not aware of the CB as an option. Consequently, a conventional boiler is installed; had the condensing type been installed, it is likely that the householder would have told others, thus helping to stimulate further demand in the wider market. Instead, demand for this technology remains small, installers do not become comfortable with the systems, economies of scale cannot be levered, the price of the CB remains relatively high so installers do not suggest them, and so on. Installation of control systems also seems to be troublesome for many installers who may not have the required skills to deal with the wiring and electronics.

The installer workforce is both ageing and contracting. Many work alone or with one or two others and most have been in the business a long time. Hardly any new apprentices are entering the trade - one estimate is as few as thirty, nationally, in 1999. In addition, the new, more rigorous, requirements for registration with CORGI (Council of Registered Gas Installers) as competent to install gas appliances safely have encouraged many to leave the industry. Consequently, for those remaining there is generally more than enough work to go round and little incentive to offer something distinctive to gain a business advantage - such as skills in energy efficiency.

In sum, the installer has little financial or longer term incentive to quote for efficient heating systems. Persuading installers otherwise will not be easy. Even forging initial contacts with the relevant institutions may be problematic - only around one third of installation businesses are members of any professional body. Those that are members seem to have rather distant relationships with their respective organisations. Installers have stronger relationships with the manufacturers of heating systems with whom they are in much more regular contact.

Manufacturers

The manufacturers do not see a commercial conflict between their efforts to stay in business and the promotion of energy efficiency. Indeed there are a number of clear economic incentives for manufacturers to promote efficiency – both by selling more units of higher value products, such as the condensing boiler or controls systems, and through increasing the rate of replacement of older boilers in the stock. Amongst the larger boiler manufacturers, new regulation on minimum efficiency standards and labelling of boilers is not viewed with concern.

Manufacturers have fairly strong relationships with the installers and go to great lengths to obtain and maintain brand loyalty through incentive schemes, provision of training and information, competitions, etc. However, manufacturers often feel that the installers make poor salesmen for their products and that their reputation may be somewhat tarnished through faulty installations. Consequently, manufacturers are highly supportive of efforts to increase the professionalism and levels of technical knowledge in the industry. To this end, the Central Heating Information Council (CHIC) has been established by the manufacturers; this body runs seminars in collaboration with the Energy Savings Trust (EST) in energy efficiency and better salesmanship. Those attending the seminar become registered as Energy Efficiency Professionals and have work allocated to them from the call centres of the EST and CHIC.

Merchants

All installers buy their supplies through builders and plumbers merchants. As long as installers request a product, merchants will continue to stock it. The decision about which product to purchase is usually taken before arrival at the merchants. Hence, at present, merchants may be considered to have a marginal role in the specification of equipment but remain an important link in the supply chain.

Conclusion

In the UK, decisions about the replacement of heating systems in existing housing are generally left to the installer. Installers have good reasons to be conservative, but, this report suggests, they have less reason to be overly concerned about suggesting equipment that may be slightly more expensive (with the current EST rebate of £200 (300 Euros), condensing storage boilers are around £50 (75 Euros) more expensive than conventional storage boilers. Condensing instantaneous boilers remain around £250 (375 Euros) more expensive with the rebate than their non-condensing equivalents). In addition, there seems no reason why installers should not, as a matter of course, make two quotes – one for the more efficient system and one for the conventional package. Householders can then choose and the installer does not risk losing the business.

The relative expense of CBs can also be reduced if bought in bulk through the merchants. However, the viability of this strategy would depend on some degree of co-operation amongst installation companies. There is a role here for the trade associations and websites in co-ordinating such co-operative purchasing of supplies.

Hence, an enthusiastic and trained installer is potentially the key to more efficient heating installations. This is also the conclusion of a recent report for the EST assessing attitudes to the cashback scheme for condensing boilers (National Energy Services, 1999), which recommends that a training course for installers be established. This should cover both the technicalities of CB installation and develop an enthusiasm for selling the idea of greater efficiency to the householder. The development of the A to G rating for new boilers displayed on the DETR's boiler efficiency database should also raise awareness of efficiency as an issue with installers. Such a label would also assist other specifiers such as architects, local authority housing officers and indeed the small number of householders who do take a more active role in specification.

However, the evidence presented here suggests that the offer of additional training is not something that many or most installers will welcome. Difficulties with training installers switches the policy onus back to the householders, who must be encouraged to ask for efficient systems. Indeed, the use of information strategies aimed at the householder rather than the installer is particularly important in creating demand for new boilers when the existing system has not yet broken down but is simply old and inefficient – an 'early replacement' strategy. A modern boiler will always be more efficient than its older replacement regardless of whether it is condensing or not. Pursuing this strategy removes the onus on the installer (to suggest the most efficient of the new systems available, i.e., CBs) whilst still achieving carbon savings. Creating demand for new systems on the grounds of inefficiency will not be easy. At present only around 5% of new installations are motivated in this way, whilst evidence presented in section 4.2.1 indicates that many householders will tolerate barely functioning heating systems indefinitely. This suggests that the main route to early replacements will be through refurbishments, extensions, kitchen refits and information that targets those situations. These motivations account for 20% of new installations.

Householders seem particularly receptive to the idea of improving the infrastructure when moving to a new home. In this respect, the proposals for the inclusion of an energy audit within a sellers' pack to be prepared by house vendors for distribution to potential buyers should be particularly effective. Equally, kitchen centres, DIY stores, builders and plumbers merchants would be appropriate places to leave leaflets and posters whilst the EST / CHIC should continue to place advertisements for their advice lines amongst the advertisements for plumbing and heating services in the Yellow Pages. Manufacturers' websites and publications should also contain references to the EST. The alternative to information strategies is regulation on domestic emissions levels allied to a strong monitoring regime. This has been done in Germany and has led to the creation of a market for more efficient heating systems - 30% of new installations are CBs (IER, 1998). In the meantime the EST rebate scheme should continue. The rebate both brings the CB payback under a five-year threshold - considered the limit at which most consumers will still find an investment attractive in the UK - and provides an official sanction to the technology. Perhaps rebates and tax breaks can also be found to provide incentives for merchants to promote efficient products in their stores.

4.3   APPLIANCES

4.3.1   Energy efficiency rebates in the UK

In the summer of 1999, the UK Energy Savings Trust (EST) ran a rebate scheme (see Appendix H) to encourage the purchase of energy efficient refrigeration. The scheme was implemented through four manufacturers who were required to make arrangements with retailers and collaboratively organise the marketing and promotion of the scheme. The rebate, either in the form of a discount or on a cash-back basis, was given for a range of A-C rated refrigeration appliances. In order to be eligible for the rebate, the only stipulation on the consumer was the trade-in of the appliance to be replaced. The scheme ran just prior to the introduction of a minimum standard in September 1999, which left only the A-C rated appliances on the market.

To gain a better understanding of the effectiveness of rebates as a policy tool for market transformation, interviews were conducted with staff and customers in three stores in Oxfordshire. In addition, a mail-out questionnaire, completed by over 700 respondents who had received the rebate, was used to quantify and validate observations from the in-store interviews. A full report of this research is presented in Appendix H. This summary identifies some areas for improvement and gives recommendations about what is desirable in future schemes.

The scheme was popular. Almost 45,000 refrigeration appliances were sold; exceeding the target. The high demand resulted in the scheme being extended by 6000 units, and funds set aside for the rebate quickly ran out despite little advertising and promotion. Both customers and sales staff confirmed what was expected, namely, that giving away money is an effective means of promoting energy efficiency when supported in a retail environment. Effects on the market are yet to be determined, but increased sales of A and B rated appliances are anticipated. In these terms the rebate programme was a success. However, more could have been achieved on other levels. Rebate schemes may be evaluated on the following criteria:

- providing financial support to bring a more costly technology in-line with the price of conventional products;
- increasing market penetration of a specific product. Lowering the price will accelerate the penetration of energy efficient technologies. Assuming the removal of old stock from use, this provides immediate environmental advantage through reduced energy consumption;
- education and promotion - the mere existence of a government-endorsed scheme provides a stamp of approval for a particular technology, thereby instilling trust in an innovation. If a programme is well publicised, this trust can be established with consumers whether they take advantage of the rebate or not. In this case, consumers can be educated through subsidy programmes if the link to energy efficiency is made clear and they receive information that implies more than a price reduction.

Financial support

Energy efficient refrigeration appliances in the UK have already reached near competitiveness with their not so efficient counter-parts. The rebate, ranging from £30 - £85 (45 – 127.5 Euros), was high compared with any discount offer and, in many cases, reduced the price to below the less efficient models. On this point the scheme was successful. However, it can be argued that given the near competitiveness of this technology, the money could have been allocated in a more effective way in order to have longer lasting effect on the market. Moreover, the value of promoting C- and even B-rated appliances, when A-C were soon to become the only products on the market, should be questioned.

Increased market penetration

In order to assess the effectiveness of the scheme in increasing market penetration beyond what would have been sold anyway, it would be necessary to compare sales of A–C rated appliances with prior sales. This kind of analysis is to be completed by the EST. For the moment, it is difficult to evaluate success on this criterion, however the EST does expect the rebate scheme to have increased sales of higher rated appliances over previous years.

Education and promotion

This scheme failed to use its potential as an educational tool. In-store observation showed there was little energy efficiency information available. The mail-out questionnaire supported this finding. Many respondents suggested the need for more information about energy efficiency in their comments about the scheme and expected this information both from in-shop information and sales staff. When asked if sales staff had explained the energy label to them, half replied they had not.

Conclusion

Although the EST rebate scheme was a success in terms of numbers of appliances sold, this analysis suggests some weaknesses. The lack of promotion of the scheme in general, and specifically the link to energy efficiency, was a missed opportunity for consumer education. To make this link to efficiency explicit, a better design would vary rebate levels with efficiency rating such that A rated appliances would receive a higher discount than Bs, and Bs higher than Cs. However, this approach is only appropriate if the scale of appliances is stretched. With just A-C rated appliances on the market, only As should be promoted. The consumer could also receive more information about efficiency when inquiring about a rebate.

This study and others identify retail staff as being highly influential in the consumer's decision: a longer term means of increasing the purchase of energy efficient appliances would be to offer financial incentives or extra commission to staff to promote and sell higher rated products. Sales staff could receive training on energy efficiency and learn how they can use it as a selling tool. In all likelihood staff would use these skills beyond the life of the commission.

4.3.2   Tumble dryers in the Netherlands

A detailed study of the Dutch gas tumble dryers market was undertaken in order to identify institutional factors affecting fuel switching policy – in this case adoption of gas rather than electric tumble dryers (full details are presented in Appendix J). Although there are no overwhelming technical barriers to entry, and the products are on the market and perform well, the introduction of this carbon efficient product into the Dutch and UK market has so far proved painfully slow: 3,000 sales since introduction in 1993 constitute only 0.14% of the market-share.

Manufacturers

The electric tumble dryer market is dominated by a small number of pan-European manufacturers. This established market structure makes it difficult for new producers with new products to make significant inroads into this market. In the Netherlands there are a limited number of gas dryer brands: Hiddokk, Coopra, Miele, Huebsch (mainly dryers for the professional market), and White Knight. Among the major European appliance manufacturers, only Miele produces gas tumble dryers. According to the company, the gas tumble dryer is expected to have a positive effect on Miele's environmental image but is not being given a high marketing priority at the moment. Electrolux, the market leader for electric tumble dryers, developed the heat pump dryer, a very efficient electric machine, instead of a gas dryer for three marketing reasons:

- the product had to be applicable world wide, thus favouring an electric product;
- the product had to be flexible, favouring a condensing dryer;
- usability - the higher price must give quality in return.

Other than Miele it seems that the other large western-European appliance manufacturers have no intention of producing gas tumble dryers.

Distribution channels

The most important distribution channel is the combined wholesale and retail or chain stores. They currently have a growing market share of about 55%. However, these stores have to be fairly selective in the products they sell – both to maintain market share and retain good trading relations with the leading manufacturers. As a consequence gas tumble dryers are not distributed by the chain stores. In addition to the chain stores, there are 'purchase combinations', whereby independent retailers co-operate for marketing purposes. The purchase combinations are responsible for about 25% of sales of domestic appliances. Retailers joining purchase combinations do not necessarily sell gas tumble dryers, but they are willing and prepared to order and deliver one. The remaining 20% is distributed via different smaller channels. These include:

- mail order firms - whose market share is decreasing;
- lease-organisations – whose market share is under pressure due to increased wealth;
- utilities – some of whom sell gas tumble dryers;
- internet sales – currently unimportant but expected to grow strongly in future.

One gas company, GGR in Tiel, succeeded in selling and installing 300 gas tumble dryers in their region. The utility organised installation of the appliances and offered subsidies on the purchase price. In addition, the project also included extra publicity and the offer of a leasing arrangement. The opinion of the utility company is that the positive contribution of the 'organised installation' was a significant factor in the success of their scheme.

Evidently, it can be very difficult for consumers to find out about gas dryers, let alone buy one because there are no effective distribution channels. Chain stores do not stock them and the other main distribution channel, the purchase combinations, does not guarantee information about the gas tumble dryer either. Consequently, the majority of potential customers will not be aware of the existence of the technology. As one of the interviewees said, "consumers have to be very persistent to obtain information about gas tumble dryers".

The effect of this is illustrated by consecutive annual surveys that have been carried out on 30,000 - 40,000 households intending to replace their current electric tumble dryer (Figure 4. 2). When asked whether they intended to replace their current dryer with a gas tumble dryer, about 6% planned to do so. Those who did not intend to buy a gas dryer were asked why not. The most common reason for not buying a gas dryer was that the respondents were unaware that this product existed. It is noticeable from this survey that awareness of gas tumble dryers has not increased over the years.

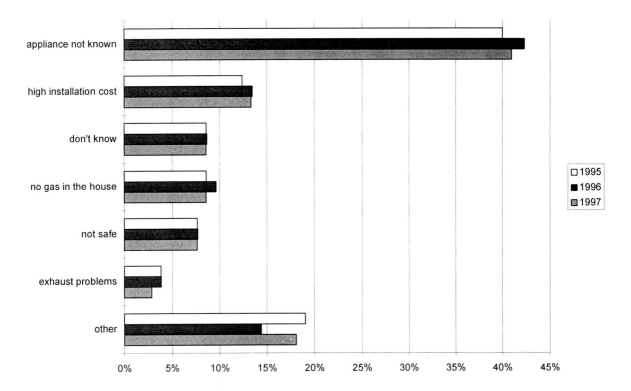

Figure 4. 2: Dutch consumers' reasons for not planning to buy a gas tumble dryer

Installation and installers

In most cases, the transportation and installation of electric tumble dryers is a service provided by the seller. Chain stores have their own delivery services, smaller retailers hire specialised delivery companies. The installation of the electrical tumble dryers does not demand special expertise; those delivering the product are also its installers. By contrast, none of the interviewees knew of chain stores or purchase combinations where delivery staff were able to install gas appliances. Thus, in most cases the installation has to be organised by the consumer. This requires extra effort and cost and causes uncertainty for the consumer. Interviews with a number of gas appliance installers showed that the likelihood of their undertaking selling and marketing activities for gas tumble dryers is low because:

- installers are originally locally oriented operators. Marketing and sales does not fit their culture;
- installers do not like single jobs: they prefer project-oriented work. The small sale of gas tumble dryers is a disadvantage;
- installers are not familiar with the gas tumble dryer and fear maintenance problems.

It is notable that these attitudes are strikingly similar to those towards condensing boilers amongst installers in the UK.

Existing government policy

The Dutch government has already taken steps towards investigating how to increase the sales of gas tumble dryers. Novem (the government energy and environment agency) has started a discussion panel to identify the problems around the introduction of the gas tumble dryers. Energy efficient domestic appliances have been subsidised since 1 November 1999 (see Section 2.3.7 for further details). The subsidy for both A-rated electric tumble dryers and gas dryers is 160 Euros. However, the Ministry of Economic Affairs recognises the complexity of the market problems for gas tumble dryer, and acknowledges that subsidies alone will not solve the fundamental problems. Nevertheless, the ministry expects some results from actions initiated by the utilities, who will support the implementation of the subsidies with regional publicity. Future government action will be aimed at utilities and chain stores, however it is not yet clear what form this will take.

Conclusion

The two major barriers to consumer purchase of gas tumble dryers have been identified as a lack of access to the product and the additional effort of arranging for installation of the gas dryer. In addition, gas dryers cost more than most venting tumble dryers, and installation imposes an additional cost (see section 3.3.5 for typical UK prices).

The starting point for government policy has to be the opening of the main retail distribution channels to gas tumble dryers. However, this is not an easy policy to design or implement. One method may be to encourage more manufacturers to enter the gas tumble dryer market. This policy would be best pursued at the EU level. Gas utilities could (financially) support investment programs. COOPRA, the Dutch importer of a gas tumble dryer, believes strongly in the positive influence of the presence of 'gas stores' which sell and install gas fired applications. In addition, installers could be encouraged to develop marketing activities for gas-fired products, so that consumers have access to the products outside of the retail structure. Due to the cultural barriers to installers undertaking such activities, this would be a longer-term option. Overcoming technical barriers will be assisted by greater numbers of installers attending the existing training courses for new gas fired products. Secondly, the government can stimulate and communicate the existence of 24-hours maintenance-services, which remove the worries about maintenance. Further opportunities lie in using new networks of installers and marketing organisations for an integrated service incorporating marketing, sales, installation and maintenance. Such a service has already been established for solar water heating systems. The special marketing and installation requirements of gas tumble dryers would also seem well suited to such schemes.

In order to overcome the barrier of installation, this process needs to be made as easy as possible for the consumer. Ideally, sales and installation would be co-ordinated by one company. Co-operation between installers and the main distribution channels must be encouraged. This means a regular dialogue between these actors and the development of new instruments such as the 'buying-contract' with recommendations for installation and references to local installation companies. Also, the internet offers new opportunities. For example, links can established for the suppliers of gas tumble dryers and specialised local installers thus minimising consumer effort in gathering information.

For new housing, the installation barrier can be eased by installation of extra gas connection points. Such a standard would significantly improve the attractiveness of the gas tumble dryers. This could be achieved by an extensive dialogue and clear policy for building companies.

4.4 FUEL SWITCHING

4.4.1 Green Electricity in the UK

Green Electricity (GE) (see Appendix G) is a generic term for electricity generated from renewable sources such as wind, water, solar, energy-from-waste and energy-from-crops (biomass). Since the autumn of 1999, GE has been available to all customers in the UK. It is usually more expensive to produce than 'brown' or conventional electricity produced from coal, oil and natural gas, and consumers are charged a premium to pay for the higher generation cost. Because of its low-to-zero carbon content, renewable energy, and consequently GE, are seen as desirable and important options for the UK's carbon reduction strategy. This section examines how much the market is being stimulated and what the policy options are to promote this product in the future.

Representatives of all 14 UK electric utilities known to be offering a GE product were contacted by telephone. They were asked to comment on the number of customers signed up for their GE product, barriers to switching to GE, their GE marketing approach and views of government's role in promoting this market (full findings are presented in Appendix G). A summary of the main observations and conclusions is provided here.

Although marketing of GE does not (and was never intended to) revolutionise the renewables industry, it does provide a potentially important means of stimulating the market. It provides consumers with the opportunity to support an environmental low carbon option through their electricity supply. For most this is a novel concept with very few aware of the choice and still fewer actually switching. Consequently, the GE market is moving slowly, with only around 10,000 households making the switch to date.

Companies view GE as a niche market and are not actively pursuing a large GE customer base. As such, the utilities see little purpose in spending on marketing. In addition, the government is providing little support to the growth of this sector and some policies may serve to brake progress if for instance, planning procedures for new renewable generation continue to stagnate. At the same time, other government policies, such as the climate change levy on non-domestic consumers, could lead to a large growth in demand which cannot be supplied. As such, a rather convoluted policy framework is in place to support the GE sector. Initial market transformation attempts have been introduced. The first step was renewable generation and distribution through the Non Fossil Fuel Obligation (NFFO – see glossary) but in the new liberalised market, unless demand grows or there is a clear strategy, there is little incentive for expanding the generation base.

Conclusion

The policy debate for this sector rests on a few important questions. Firstly, whether to support green electricity or greener brown electricity, secondly, whether consumer pull or supply push is the answer to a take-off of this market, and finally, what are the policy implications of this?

Admittedly, the market is still young and most consumers have only had the option of switching to GE for a few months. As experience elsewhere shows, more time, something in the order of 2 years, will be required to achieve a 1-2% participation rate amongst domestic consumers (Farhar and Houston, 1996). An important barrier in the domestic market is that most consumers are unaware of the environmental consequences of their electricity use, and so do not understand the benefit of switching to green. Even those who are aware may not know GE is an option. Indeed even those who do know about GE may be confused by products on offer and have no means of comparing products. One information policy aiming to address these issues is a Power Content Label that could be applied to all electricity bills. This shows the power mix provided by a particular utility in comparison with the national average. It provides the consumer with important information about where electricity is being generated and has been introduced by certain utilities in the US (Davis and Tutt, 1996). Linking generation to carbon emissions would take the message one step further.

The renewable energy industry fear that GE offers provide no real substitute for the solid backing of renewables given by national support programmes, such as the NFFO. Outside NFFO there is very little new renewable energy generation. And even within NFFO, support is often impeded by complicated planning procedures. Whether push or pull, what this market requires is a clear strategy and government commitment to achieve its renewables targets. A holistic policy approach that addresses both the supply and demand side can be developed but requires the integration and commitment of a number of government departments to achieve a greener energy future for the UK.

4.4.2   Natural Gas in Portugal

As mentioned in section 3.3.2 and 3.3.3, there is a political will in Portugal to expand the natural gas (NG) network. To assess the prospects for domestic connection to the network and the conversion of existing appliance to the new fuel (either from LPG or electrical appliances) 25 detailed audits were carried out with households who had made the switch. Also, each individual in the household was asked to complete a questionnaire. This yielded 86 questionnaires. In addition, interviews were conducted with representatives of all the main actors (equipment suppliers, manufacturers, householders) and a further survey of a random sample of 106 householders was also completed.

The surveys suggest that there does not appear to be much resistance to switching to NG for water heating. When switching from electrically heated, NG is generally viewed as cheaper. When switching from bottled gas it is viewed as both cheaper and less trouble - particularly amongst elderly people who dislike the effort required in continually fetching and installing the new bottles. As one householder put it, "I am tired of transporting bottles of gas; on top of all that, the gas only runs out when I need to take a bath or to cook!" The presence of pressurised bottles of gas within the building fabric is also seen as more dangerous than having the piped variety. However, the North of the country has traditionally relied more on electricity for its water heating and hence greater levels of concern about safety aspects of gas are found here – whether it be bottled or piped. There seems to be a greater resistance to replacing electrical heating with gas fired space heating. Amongst those who had had natural gas installed, 76% were happy to heat their water with NG rather than electric. Further details can be found in appendices P and Q.

4.5   DISCUSSION AND CONCLUSIONS

Consumption is not the isolated act of an individual – choices about appliances, heating systems and fuel take place in complex social, institutional and cultural settings. The importance of acknowledging these factors has been clearly demonstrated. If more energy and carbon efficient equipment is to be brought into the home, complexity must be recognised and incorporated into the policy process. It is not sufficient to label an appliance or provide a rebate, if other constituents of the choice are unsupportive. The retail environment, the motivation of the installer, the philosophy of the utility, must all be working towards the same objective – more efficient equipment and lower carbon choices. This recognition is helpful in explaining why individual policies are unsuccessful. However, the existence of a chain of decision-makers means that policies must be part of a comprehensive strategy if they are to be truly influential. That is the challenge.

The five case studies in this chapter identified some common themes:

- the consumer at home is often dependent on a single advisor. The calibre of the heating installer (or retail sales person, solar panel sales person or double glazing representative) and the way the householder responds to this individual's advice is crucial in determining what is purchased. The relationship is between the poorly informed householder and an 'expert'. Therefore, if society wants more efficiency delivered, it should assist the householder by making sure the expert is well informed and educated;
- the consumer in the shop can choose from a range of experts – different salespeople, different retail outlets – and can even ignore them all and make an independent choice. However, this choice can only be made from the items on sale – if the stores do not stock A-rated appliances or gas-fired tumble dryers, the consumer cannot buy them. The marketing strategy of the retail chain needs to be positively supportive of energy efficiency and green choices, so that the products are available, and the sales staff promoting them. The use of rebates and commission bonuses are good ways to enforce the message in the short term, but commitment and education are the only longer term guarantees of environmental support;
- the delicate interplay between the consumer and the producer was demonstrated with green electricity and the gas tumble dryer market. Householders cannot demand or purchase something they do not know is there. And utilities will not strongly promote a product until they have confidence in the existence of a market. It is less a case of 'push' or 'pull' and more an example of gentle, hesitant steps forward, together.

The policies that will deliver the potential carbon reductions depend upon a society with shared environmental concerns and commitments and an institutional framework which not only encourages efficient choices, but is seen to do so. Education and awareness, advice and exhortation, have a stronger role to play than has been identified in previous studies and thus will be a theme of the scenario in Chapter 6. First, Chapter 5 examines the policy components and recent experience.

CHAPTER 5: POLICY TOOLKIT

This chapter brings together the current status of market transformation practice and theory for energy efficiency, and discusses the ways in which it could develop to include fuel switching. The purpose is not to be prescriptive about which policy instruments must be used, but rather to explore the different options, their advantages and disadvantages in different situations, and to outline some innovative new approaches. The importance of recognising the role of different actors, as stressed in Chapter 4, is taken into account, as is the necessity of a sophisticated understanding of consumption in order to design effective policy.

First market transformation is introduced as a policy philosophy, and the stages in market transformation are outlined (Section 5.1). Then there is further discussion on individual policy instruments, and in particular different methods of achieving the same policy goal (Section 5.2). The policy considerations around fuel switching are then outlined and attention is focussed on the broadening scope of policy once fuel choice enters the policy arena (Section 5.3). For both energy efficiency and fuel switching policies, the question of measuring and verifying savings due to new policy is critical (Section 5.4). The role of energy prices and taxes is an important issue, as is the link between energy taxes and market transformation (Section 5.5). Finally, the over-arching issues in designing a policy package: cost, effectiveness, equity and certainty of savings (and the links and between these) are explored (Section 5.6). This chapter provides the policy toolkit from which the scenarios in Chapter 6 are developed.

5.1   INTRODUCTION TO MARKET TRANSFORMATION

5.1.1   Market transformation and energy efficiency

The philosophy underlying the policy packages in previous ECI work, *2MtC*, can be characterised as 'market transformation'. The aim of market transformation is to produce significant and lasting change in the efficiency of new appliances more quickly than would have happened without intervention. It is carried out using a range of policy tools at different stages of a product's development, recognising a number of important factors, such as range of efficiency on the current market, technical potential, costs of efficiency, rates of change and the extent of competition. Policy tools used include minimum standards, industry agreements, procurement, subsidies and rebates and labels. It is a policy-making process which works with the market within a strategic framework, as described briefly below (Table 5. 1). The main implementers of a market transformation strategy are the EU and national governments.

Table 5. 1: Policy instruments for a market transformation strategy

Purpose	Policy instruments
Make efficiency transparent	- First develop measurement standards, then mandatory efficiency testing, usually followed by labels or other means of ranking products

Build the market for existing efficient technologies, i.e. promote best practice	- educate and inform consumers / retailers / installers / manufacturers on efficiency / environment issues
	- provide economic incentives to increase sales:
	    rebates to consumers / retailers / installers / manufacturers
	    differing VAT rates depending on efficiency
	    increase price competition at efficient end of market
	    aggregated purchase

Encourage new, super-efficient technologies	- technology procurement - research and development support - set ambitious standards for the best category on the energy label and revise regularly in conjunction with minimum standards
Remove least efficient appliances from market	- mandatory minimum standards - industry agreements

Market transformation is, to a large extent, the policy paradigm that has been adopted by the EU and many of the member states to increase the energy efficiency of traded goods and it is growing in popularity and acceptance. However, this is not to say that all the actions undertaken by governments or their agents fit within this strategy. For example, the design of some of the UK EST's subsidies for cold appliances are driven by the rules of energy efficiency funding programmes and not by the requirement to contribute to market transformation (Chapter 4). Neither does it imply that governments are doing all that they could to further market transformation.

In *2MtC* the market transformation approach was used to design policy packages per appliance group which would ensure that ETP technology was introduced as quickly as possible, whilst keeping costs to manufacturers and consumers low. Also, by targeting rebates and subsidies at low-income households, a market transformation strategy can incorporate equity considerations.

For all forms of energy efficiency policy, particular difficulties are faced when the actor being targeted does not have a natural interest in the energy efficiency of the product. Some key examples of this are:
- house builders providing equipment, for which the owner pays the running costs;
- landlords providing equipment, for which the tenant pays the running costs;
- installers specifying boilers, for which the householder pays the running costs (as Chapter 4 explored in detail).

Although minimum standards / industry agreements will affect these actors, it is very difficult to target policies that try to build the market for more efficient appliances at these groups. This broadly leaves policy makers with the options of trying to create specific market incentives for these actors (e.g., payments to installers for installing efficient boilers), and educating and informing both these actors and the user of the equipment in order to create a demand for efficiency.

5.1.2 Market transformation and fuel switching

To date, market transformation has been about creating a market in energy efficiency, not a market in carbon emissions. At present most consumers are likely to be ignorant of the difference in carbon dioxide emissions between gas and electricity. Thus, fuel switching is unlikely to occur through the actions of the public, without external stimulus and education. Whether it would be effective to try to create such a market in some way (discussed further in Chapter 6), or to impose a carbon tax to give a financial signal (discussed further in Section 5.5), is clearly one of the key questions. Alternatively, it may be simpler and more effective to set fuel switching targets (in the same way that targets are set for CHP and renewable electricity production), and design policy to meet those goals. However, familiar market transformation policy instruments could be used to encourage fuel switching from electricity to gas, and these are discussed briefly below.

As energy labels are currently being developed for gas ovens, and may well eventually be applied to other gas appliances, the energy label could be used to signal relative carbon emissions to the consumer. However, there are a number of problems with this idea (discussed in detail in Section 5.3.2). Whether or not energy labels are used, education of consumers and other actors around the relative carbon emissions of different fuels will have to be undertaken.

Subsidies for gas appliances (tumble dryers) are already available in the Netherlands, although the policy makers themselves doubt these will significantly increase the market share of gas tumble dryers. Given the complex barriers to greater adoption of gas equipment discussed in Chapter 4, subsidies are probably a minor part of a necessary policy package.

Technology procurement is not necessary where gas alternatives to electric appliances already exist, as for water heating, cooking and clothes drying. However, the development of gas systems within a house, which make connecting to gas as easy as electricity, currently being researched in the Netherlands, might be worthwhile. This would enable the householder to connect an appliance safely, without requiring a professional installer.

As shown in Chapter 3, the carbon emissions of the most efficient electric appliances can approach those of gas appliances (given UK, NL and PO carbon intensity of electricity). Minimum standards of efficiency could be set such that everything except the most efficient electric competitor with gas appliances was eliminated from the market, thus effectively transforming the market in favour of lower carbon appliances without the necessity of favouring a particular fuel. This idea is developed further in Chapter 6.

In conclusion, market transformation policy instruments can be extended from energy efficiency to carbon efficiency in many cases. However, fuel switching raises policy issues which are outside the scope of market transformation policy (Section 5.3) and new approaches are also required.

5.1.3   Market transformation and energy conservation

As demonstrated in Chapter 2, EU policy is at present oriented towards energy efficiency rather than energy conservation, despite the need to reduce carbon emissions. If energy conservation was the goal of EU policy, market transformation could still have a part to play in delivering such policy goals. For example, the EU could decide to award the next round of energy labels on cold appliances on the basis of energy consumption rather than efficiency, thus awarding more favourable energy labels to smaller appliances. In this case, the familiar tools of market transformation could be used, at least to some degree, to promote lower energy consuming appliances. However, there is clearly a tension in trying to use market instruments to reduce demand for consumer goods. A policy of persuading consumers to do without certain goods or services could only come from a more radical philosophy than market transformation. This is discussed further in Chapter 6.

5.2   MARKET TRANSFORMATION POLICY INSTRUMENTS

5.2.1   Making efficiency transparent

With energy efficiency, whether for gas or electric appliances, the efficiency of a product first has to be made transparent. This information has been provided to the consumer via energy labels for some products, such as wet and cold appliances, and these labels have been proven to be effective in influencing consumer decisions (Winward *et al.*, 1998). It has been accepted that mandatory labelling systems are preferable to voluntary labels for energy efficiency, hence the energy label. However, once a test procedure is in place, products can be ranked without necessarily being labelled, two examples of this are given below. Enabling comparison of efficiency is a necessary pre-cursor to introducing policy to encourage the best and remove the worst from the market. Not only that, it also empowers the consumer to buy efficiency, and persuades retailers and manufacturers to compete on efficiency as an important product characteristic.

National governments can provide information on ranking of products in the absence of an EU energy label. This information can be targeted at the key decision makers for that product. For example, a boiler database was launched by the UK government in September 1999 (www.sedbuk.com). It was developed primarily to help assessors using the government's Standard Assessment Procedure for energy rating of dwellings, which must be carried out for all new buildings. The database is also intended to assist purchasers of boilers and central heating systems. Data for current production models have been provided by boiler manufacturers, and information on almost 1000 boilers is currently available. As a simple guide to efficiency, a temporary scheme has been created with seasonal efficiency bands assigned to boilers on an A to G scale. The scheme is temporary and will be withdrawn when an EU scheme for boiler energy labelling is introduced. Another example of providing information on ranking without attaching a label to product is the provision, in the UK, of independent test data on the power demand of TVs is via a government web site (www.mtprog.com).

5.2.2   Building the market for efficiency via price reduction

One of the key means of encouraging greater uptake of efficient technologies, is lowering the purchase price of the most efficient. The other means identified in Table 5. 1 is increased education of consumers and other market actors. Four methods of lowering price will be considered: subsidies; aggregated purchase; reduced levels of VAT; increased price competition. These policies are the part of a market transformation strategy that can have the greatest cost to national government. Thus not only is it important to consider their potential effectiveness, cost-effectiveness is also key.

Subsidies

In designing a subsidy programme for market transformation several key issues have to be decided:

- the level of subsidy;
- whether the subsidy is to be targeted, for example to low income consumers;
- to whom the subsidy should be paid: consumers, retailers or manufacturers;
- the specification of equipment to be subsidised;
- the scale of the subsidy programme, i.e., how many subsidies are to be offered and for how long.

All of these decisions have to be made on a case-by-case basis, and it is difficult to develop general rules. It has been suggested that it is necessary to support up to 20% of the market in order to ensure that there is a sufficient manufacturing base to guarantee economies of scale and price competition (DECADE, 1997). However, the financial commitment that this would entail makes it seem overly ambitious unless the subsidies also had social benefits, by, for example, being targeted at low-income households.

In order to assess the effects of subsidies it necessary to consider both the direct and indirect effects. The simplest assumption to make about the direct effect of a subsidy is that in its absence the consumer would have bought an appliance of average efficiency, thus the savings are the difference between the subsidised appliance and the average. This does not take account of any 'free rider' effects; consumers taking the subsidy who would have bought a more efficient appliance in any case. Nor does it account for 'free drivers', consumers who are inspired by the example of the policy and respond without taking the rebate. Subsidies that are paid directly to manufacturers or retail staff are more cost-effective than those given to consumers in some cases because of multiplier effects. However, delivering subsidies in this way does not necessarily help to educate the consumer. It is more difficult to estimate the indirect effects of subsidies. If subsides are acting to transform the market, they should be contributing to building the market for efficient appliances in general, and reducing the price of these appliances in future. Whether this is likely to be the case must involve a judgement of the state of the market, the scale of the scheme and whether it is large enough to have a market transformation effect.

Aggregated purchase

A new policy tool, currently being developed at EU level, is aggregated purchase (also known as co-operative procurement). The aim of aggregated purchase is to increase the market share of the most efficient appliances on the market. By gathering together buyers (whether purchasers of the technology or retailers) considerable purchasing power can be exerted on manufacturers to provide efficient appliances at a cheaper price. A large guaranteed market in turn allows manufacturers to access economies of scale.

The current pilot project (ICECAP) relates to energy efficient fridge-freezers. A research consortium from ten member states is working to bring together manufacturers of super efficient 'Energy+' fridge-freezers with retailers who wish to sell them. By providing information, encouragement and the promise of positive publicity, the researchers hope to increase the market for Energy+ appliances. The target efficiency has been set at a level which will ensure the Energy+ models comply with the new ecolabel criteria (efficiency index of 0.42, see Glossary). Initial indications are that both manufacturers and retailers are reacting positively to this initiative.

With motivated buyers and responsive manufacturers it appears that aggregated purchase may have an important part to play in market transformation. Certainly, compared with subsidies it could prove to be very cost-effective. However, it is too early to assess how successful the Energy+ scheme will be, and it is probably best not to claim too much for this policy tool until its effectiveness has been proved.

Altered levels of VAT

In principle it is possible to alter the rates of VAT (value added tax) depending on the efficiency of the product. Several European countries have already reduced or removed VAT on building insulation materials, however, none has yet altered VAT on lights, water heating equipment or appliances. VAT alterations affect the whole market. The cost of removing VAT to the government could be considerable. Reducing VAT to 5% on, say, A rated appliances in the UK would entail a 12.5% price drop. As the price drop took effect, and sales of efficient appliances increased the revenue lost to government would increase. Thus it would be in governments' interest to ensure that the ranking of appliances was regularly updated, so that the percentage of the market being supported in this way did not become too large.

Increased price competition

By increasing competition on price at the efficient end of the market it should be possible to secure a permanent decrease in the prices of efficient equipment. There has been an excellent example of this in Denmark. The Danish Electricity Savings Trust's 'A Club' has set up a web site for information about A-rated appliances (www.hvidevarepriser.dk). The site is accessible by individual retailers who can supply prices for the appliances to the site. As a result of publicising this information on the web, the recommended retail price quoted by these retailers went down by 20% within three weeks (Karbo, pers. comm.). The Trust has put considerable resources into publicising the web site; it now receives around 1,300 hits per day, which is impressive particularly in comparison with the estimated 3,300 cold and wet appliances sold per day in Denmark. This represents a particularly dramatic example of the power of information to increase competition and help reduce the price of efficient appliances to consumers.

Discussion

All of the mechanisms mentioned have the potential to deliver reductions in the price of efficient equipment. Subsidies and aggregated purchase tend to be temporary in nature, whereas VAT alteration and particularly increased price competition should have a permanent effect on the market. The costs of altering VAT may be hard for government to control, whereas the budget for subsidy schemes can be fixed. Given the great success of increased price competition in Denmark, it would seem that this relatively low cost scheme is worthy of consideration by all member states.

5.2.3 Removing the least efficient from the market

As illustrated in Table 5. 1, there are two alternative approaches to removing the least efficient goods from the market: mandatory minimum standards and industry agreements. There is an ongoing debate around the use of minimum standards, which are resisted by some stakeholders. In its strategy document on energy efficiency, the Commission advocates the wider use of industry agreements, provided they fulfil the requirements of the Communication on Environmental Agreements (European Commission, DGXI, 1996).

The Commission has preferred industry agreements essentially for practical reasons. They are seen as more flexible, less resource intensive and quicker to implement – they meet with less resistance from manufacturers and they do not have to involve the Council or Parliament (Bertoldi *et al.*, 1998). However, theoretically they seem less attractive. A minimum standard includes all products sold on the EU market, whereas an industry agreement only includes the products of participating manufacturers, allowing non-participants to continue to sell products (usually imported) that do not meet the target efficiency level. In addition, industry agreements do not have the legal sanctions (in case of non-compliance) that minimum standards do, nor necessarily the independent monitoring. Being quicker to implement does not imply more rapid achievement of savings if the targets agreed are only marginally more ambitious than the underlying trend. Finally, industry agreements do not provide a long-term framework for decision-making for a variety of product groups. They are negotiated piecemeal with different industry sectors, targets set with reference only to that particular product, and for a relatively short time span. And the question remains as to whether manufacturers will voluntarily agree to tough efficiency targets, as they are unlikely to see this as being in their interest.

To overcome these problems, the Commission needs to introduce a framework directive on minimum standards. This would be enabling legislation that sets out general principles for further regulation, without the need to refer back to the Council or Parliament (as is already the case for energy labels). Not only will it provide a long-term strategy for efficiency improvements, it can also provide many of the practical advantages that come with industry agreements, particularly speed of decision-making. During the negotiation period for minimum standards and industry agreements there is compromise between manufacturers and technical experts. Manufacturers are very powerful in the negotiation process, in a way that consumer and environmental groups are not. The Commission needs to be able to negotiate from a position of strength: a framework directive would give it that strength - even if industry agreements continue to be the preferred policy instrument in practice.

However, in some situations minimum standards are not appropriate. This is particularly true for proposals such as a Corporate Average Bulb Efficiency (DECADE, 1997) which rely on manufacturers producing an agreed proportion of efficient bulbs, and not on outlawing all inefficient bulbs. This would also be true for the policy on boilers suggested in Chapter 6. In addition, in order to encourage fuel switching to gas, agreements with manufacturers could require them to produce a certain percentage of gas appliances, where gas and electricity are competitive fuels.

5.2.4   Education and training

The role of education and training was stressed throughout Chapter 4, and its importance in terms of delivering carbon savings must not be under-rated. As with developing a method of ranking, educating and motivating consumers, retailers, manufacturers, installers and other actors underpins all other policy measures in the market transformation toolkit.

5.3   FUEL SWITCHING POLICY

The main focus in this section is on fuel switching from electricity to natural gas, although the opportunities provided by renewables are of increasing importance, both household-based options like solar thermal (see Glossary) and collective schemes through green electricity. There is concern that by encouraging a switch to natural gas people will be locked into a carbon-based fuel, as opposed to concentrating on providing renewable alternatives. However, given the very slow progress towards generation of renewable electricity in many EU countries, gas is likely to remain the lower carbon fuel, compared with electricity, for at least 10-20 years. Switching to natural gas is thus a valuable component of a lower carbon policy in many countries in the short to medium term at least.

5.3.1   Comparison between fuel switching and energy efficiency

The policy challenge for fuel switching is not the same as that for energy efficiency. The pricing of fuel already generally works in favour of gas use. The challenge, on the demand side, is to persuade those consumers who have not connected to the gas network to do so, and those who are connected to use gas for as many functions within the house as possible. This is also in the interest of the gas industry. Policy considerations include the way in which the decision to change fuels is made, as well as the additional costs, within the house, of providing a gas supply to the new equipment. To effect accelerated network expansion, policy boundaries extend to the choices of and regulations imposed upon the gas utility.

Thus once policy moves beyond efficient use of electricity to gas use and fuel switching, a broader approach is required if the maximum savings are to be achieved. The policy realms are schematically portrayed in Figure 5.1: the inner circle is the appliance, the second circle extends to the system for water (and space) heating, the third circle is the whole house (its infrastructure and energy demand) and the outer circle includes national fuel choices (fuel availability, the supply system and policies on renewable energy sources). The breadth of the policy agenda is part of the debate. Including gas and comparing between fuels also moves the policy debate from a focus on energy to a focus on carbon dioxide: unsurprisingly, as that is the objective/target for the new policies. Achieving the Kyoto target, let alone more rigorous future ones, requires the widest possible access to policy options.

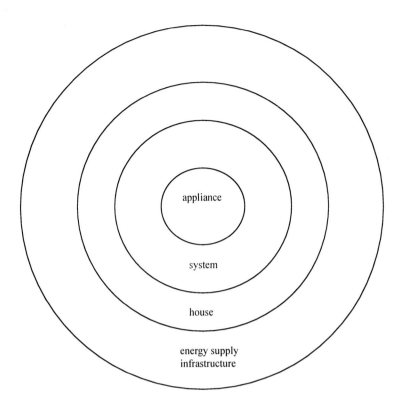

Figure 5. 1: Schematic representation of policy realms

5.3.2   Appliances - labels for gas appliances

The recent and ongoing studies on gas appliances, and the question of fuel switching raises the issue of how these two fuels are to be treated under an energy-labelling scheme. One option would be not to have labels for gas appliances, this is the route that has been followed in the USA and Canada, and as demonstrated earlier, products can be ranked without being labelled. In general it has been thought inappropriate to apply labels where product development is extremely rapid (consumer electronics) or where no significant range of efficiency exists. This is not the case for gas ovens, and so labels should be introduced for these; the decision on whether to apply labels to other gas appliances should be taken on a case-by-case basis.

The key problem with comparative labelling for gas and electric appliances is that their relative rankings change depending on the unit of measurement chosen (Table 5. 2). For instance, a gas appliance generally uses more delivered energy but less primary energy than an electric appliance. As discussed earlier (Section 5.3.2) this will also vary between member states, depending on the carbon intensity of electricity, and will vary through time as fuel sources for electricity production change.

Table 5. 2: Comparative measures for gas and electric appliances, UK, NL and PO

Measurement	Gas	Electricity
delivered energy consumption	more	less
primary energy consumption	less	more
carbon dioxide emissions	less	more
running costs	less	more

The energy label contains two key pieces of information:
- the relative ranking of an appliance – the A-G scale;
- the absolute energy consumption of an appliance under the test procedure.

Options for A-G scale

The advantages and disadvantages of various options for the A-G scale on an energy label are set out (Table 5. 3). This assumes that absolute energy consumption for gas appliances is reported as delivered energy in the units with which the consumer is already familiar, both because they are used on other labels and because they are shown on meters and bills.

Table 5. 3: Options for A-G scale on gas and electric Energy Labels

Options for A-G scale	Advantages	Disadvantages
a common scale based on primary energy or carbon	• indicates true environmental cost of each fuel to consumer • may help in fuel switching away from electricity	• all gas appliances bunched together at top end of scale, all electric at bottom • problems of changing ratio of primary to delivered over time, plus different ratios in each member state • scale does not match energy figures
a common scale based on delivered energy	• scale will match energy consumption figures	• misleading to consumer in terms of environmental impact of different fuels • all electric appliances bunched together at top end of scale, all gas at bottom • may encourage fuel switching towards electricity
separate scales based on delivered energy	• scale will match energy consumption figures for separate fuels • makes use of full range of A-G scale for both electric and gas appliances • neutral on fuel switching, thus should be more acceptable than other options to manufacturers	• doesn't help (and may even hinder) the consumer make environmental fuel switching choice • need to design distinctive gas Energy Label to minimise confusion

From this analysis, a good option would seem to be separate scales based on delivered energy. This option offers useful information to the consumer, avoids very considerable practical problems involved in using primary energy as the basis for labelling, and should be more acceptable to industry than other options. In addition, it will fulfil the primary aim of the labelling directive in enabling the consumer to choose a more efficient appliance. However, under this scheme, energy labelling would not be an instrument of fuel switching policy.

A variation on this option, not included in the table above, would be to align the scales differently for each fuel. For instance, the electricity scale could be predominantly D-G, whereas gas, initially, could extend to B. This would require manufacturers of electrical appliance to produce equipment of greater energy efficiency to qualify for a higher category, therefore, justly minimising their environmental impact.

If it is thought critical that energy labels contribute to fuel switching, then the option to choose would be that of using a common scale based on primary energy or carbon.

Options for reported absolute energy use

For gas, the simplest and best option is to use the same principles as applied to the measurement of electricity consumption. The values should be:

• based on delivered energy
• reported in units used by the consumer

Reporting energy consumption in the units on the consumer's gas bill across the EU will require values to be reported in both kWh and m^3 (Kasanen, 1999). This could be misleading, as the consumer, seeing higher gas consumption in kWh than for a similar electric appliance, may make incorrect inferences about environmental impact and running cost. As an alternative, it has been suggested that the units used for test consumption on the label should be MJ. However, although the concern about kWh figures leading to confusion is valid, presenting the information in units the consumer is unfamiliar with would clearly be unhelpful and would be likely to lead to greater confusion. Careful design of a gas energy label, supporting literature, training for sales staff etc., could help alert the consumer to the need for caution when making direct comparisons.

5.3.3   Whole house approaches

Setting standards for new housing represents a considerable opportunity for governments to encourage the adoption of lower carbon solutions. Minimum insulation standards are already included in the building codes of all EU member states. However, there is the opportunity to move beyond simply the building shell and energy efficiency to specify the carbon efficiency of the dwelling. This would include consideration of primarily the water and space heating systems, but could also include the lights and appliances installed. Whole house approaches could also contribute to encouraging fuel-switching from electricity to gas and renewable options.

In the UK, Netherlands and Portugal, there is a system of control on new housing which ensures that required standards of energy efficiency increase over time. Although it is difficult to directly compare the systems, it is clear that the standards required in the Netherlands are more stringent than those in the UK and Portugal. The Dutch energy performance co-efficient required in 2000 is likely to encourage greater use of heat pumps and solar water heating, as well as increased use of more conventional efficiency measures. In addition, target values are set in terms of primary energy, which approximately reflects carbon dioxide emissions, thus encouraging a switch to lower carbon options such as district heating. As requirements continue to increase, more use of lower carbon fuels and renewable energy is likely to follow.

However, in all three countries, the number of houses newly built each year is far lower than the number that changes hands, and is a small proportion of the total stock. Therefore, the bigger challenge is how to apply policy to the existing housing stock. In the UK, there have been proposals for mandatory energy audits to be carried out when properties are sold. The idea is that not only would householders receive specific advice on improving the energy efficiency of the property they are buying, but that eventually energy efficiency would be reflected in house prices. In the UK, some building societies include an energy audit with the building survey details, and in Austria, a trial is being carried out attaching energy labels to houses (Eggar and Dell, 1999). These ideas could be extended from energy efficiency to carbon reduction.

In addition, the use of gas could be consolidated by requiring that all new homes within the gas network, have gas space and water heating installed along with ample connection points for additional gas appliances (e.g. tumble dryer). Where a fitted kitchen is provided, gas oven and hob would be installed. This would be more radical than current arrangements for connection to district heating in the Netherlands, where there is only a general requirement for new houses to be connected to district heating if local governments have decided on a heat infrastructure. If in a new building area project developers, energy companies and the community decide on implementing a heat infrastructure, all houses are connected to this infrastructure and generally tied to heat purchase for contract periods of say 25 years. In the light of the coming liberalisation of energy market (for small consumers) energy companies are eager to put down such an infrastructure to tie clients before liberalisation starts. Whether this is a substantial development remains to be seen.

5.3.4   Energy supply infrastructure

There has been considerable emphasis within Europe on the use of gas on the supply side for electricity generation as one of the means of reaching Kyoto targets, at least for those countries where more carbon intensive fossil fuels such as coal and oil are currently used for electricity production. For the UK,

Netherlands and Portugal, where the carbon intensity of electricity is relatively high, there is a good justification for a similar emphasis on the use of gas at a household level. However, given the varying carbon intensities of electricity across the EU (Table 5. 4), this is not a policy which has universal application - unlike energy efficiency.

The gas debate opens up a further set of issues in relation to the remit of the different policy makers. Natural gas is not equally available throughout the EU; 1% of households use natural gas in Sweden, up to 96% in the Netherlands (Table 5. 4). The opportunities for switching between fuels therefore varies, and means that Europe-wide policies on comparative fuels are not applicable. The gas networks in each EU country, and plans for expansion, are discussed further in Chapter 7 and the Country Picture supporting material.

Table 5. 4: Households with natural gas and carbon content of electricity

Country	% with gas (1997-99)	Electricity kg C/kWh (1995)
Austria	37	0.06
Belgium	55	0.09
Denmark	12	0.22
Finland	2	0.09
France	41	0.02
Germany	42	0.16
Greece	0.2	0.24
Ireland	27	0.20
Italy	70	0.14
Netherlands	97	0.17
Portugal	3	0.16
Spain	26	0.12
Sweden	1	0.01
UK	82	0.14
EU	**48%**	**0.11**

Source: as for Table 7.1

As the carbon content of emissions per unit of electricity vary across Europe, the benefits of, and reasons for, fuel switching are nationally specific. Policies on fuel switching have to be the responsibility of the member state rather than the European Commission at present. However, due to the effects of liberalisation and privatisation, the electricity market is moving from separate national markets to a market covering most of the EU. This means that even if electricity savings take place in a country with low carbon intensity (such as Sweden or France), it might well be that significant carbon emissions are avoided elsewhere as the saved electricity could be exported. Nevertheless, for the time being it seems most appropriate to identify the state as the main actor on fuel switching.

At state level, however, there are several reasons for a reluctance to promote one fuel over another. The priorities vary in different member states, but include:
- the problems of favouring one nationalised industry over another, and of favouring one private company over another;
- the problems of agreeing the units of measurement (e.g., price, primary energy, delivered energy, useful energy and, now, carbon dioxide emissions) as this affects the comparison (Section 5.3.2);
- changing conditions over time, for instance, the carbon content of electricity has dropped by 30% in the last seven years in the UK;
- the need to retain the goodwill of both gas and electricity industries where they fund energy savings organisations, as is the case with the UK EST;
- the concerns of those industries that manufacture products solely for one fuel, including utilities that sell only one fuel.

Some of these barriers may be reduced as, increasingly, utilities sell both fuels to domestic customers and the retail outlets are energy centres, rather than gas or electricity showrooms.

The reluctance to promote fuel switching to natural gas does not exist in all EU countries. For example, the Danish government has set up the Electricity Saving Trust with the express objective of reducing electricity demand, particularly through fuel switching (www.ens.dk). However, in the UK fuel switching is not, and has not (Boardman, 1991), been encouraged either specifically by government or by other energy agencies, such as the electricity and gas regulator, OFGEM (Office of gas and electricity markets) or the EST. Nor has fuel switching been promoted by the gas utilities, even though they would benefit most.

Green electricity
The first stage in transforming the electricity market to green electricity has been taken in the UK by the development of a government-sponsored award label for green electricity. In addition, a government White Paper proposes an obligation on electricity suppliers to purchase 5% from renewables by 2003 and 10% by 2010. In the Netherlands, the energy sector has agreed (voluntarily) to buy 3% of electricity from renewables by the end of 2000. Of the three countries, Portugal has electricity with the greatest renewable content (about 40%), at present there are no plans to try and increase the renewable proportion of generation by marketing green electricity to consumers. However, there are strong supply side financial incentives to set up new wind and mini-hydro power plants. The electricity generated in these power plants receives a price premium (based on avoided carbon dioxide emissions) of 0.03 Euros/kWh.

As discussed in Chapter 4, renewable energy policy can encompass the domestic demand side by making consumers aware of how green their electricity is, and enabling them to buy green. This complements supply side actions that, for example, require a certain percentage of renewable generation.

5.4   ASSESSING THE EFFECTIVENESS OF POLICIES

Increasing attention is being given to monitoring and evaluation of the effects of market transformation policies. The ultimate test of policy is whether domestic sector carbon dioxide emissions are being reduced or restrained as necessary to meet Kyoto commitments. Thus the overall effectiveness of government policy measures can be monitored fairly straightforwardly via national energy consumption and carbon emission statistics. However, market transformation policies are generally intended to take effect on the product level and it is at this level that their effectiveness must be initially judged.

For each policy there are two key questions:
• did the policy meet its targets?
• how much energy was / will be saved as a result of the policy?

The first question is usually much easier to answer than the second. For example, it is far easier to assess whether a rebate has been taken up or an industry agreement's efficiency targets have been met than it is to monitor or estimate the energy savings, direct and indirect, that will result from these policies.

To answer the second question, it is always necessary to have a good estimate of what would have happened in the absence of the policy. Given that, for many appliances, efficiency has been improving in the absence of policy over recent years, an improvement in efficiency is not sufficient to prove a policy has been successful. Only savings, which go beyond what would have been expected under reference scenarios, should be ascribed to policy actions. The construction of a reference scenario is key to estimating the energy saving effects of policy, and is one of the areas over which disagreement often arises.

In addition, it is necessary to look beyond product-level energy efficiency to determine whether a policy is leading to energy savings. For example, in order to make energy savings from the cold appliance sector, not only does energy efficiency have to counteract growth in household numbers and increased levels of ownership, it also has to overcome the trend towards ownership of different, more energy consuming types of cold appliances. These considerations should of course be taken into account at the policy design as well as the evaluation stage.

5.4.1 Monitoring methodologies

EU policies are of a scale and ambition where the effect of a policy on total energy consumption can (at least in theory) be measured or inferred through analysis of sales and acquisitions data. This is not usually the case for national policies - as illustrated in Chapter 2, many of the UK national policies have not been on a sufficient scale to have measurable effects beyond the household level. This is not to say that the success of smaller scale policies cannot be monitored, simply that their effect on national energy savings can only be estimated, which makes transparent and robust savings estimation guidelines crucial.

There are a number of ways of testing the effectiveness of two EU policies, energy labels and minimum standards (Table 5. 5). Various types of evidence are needed to determine whether the policy has been implemented effectively, let alone whether energy savings have resulted. For energy labels on cold appliances, the first three types of evidence were collected in a study for the Commission (Winward *et al.*, 1998). This study also made a number of suggestions that would ease future evaluations of effectiveness, including revising the test procedure, sharing independent test data across Europe and public deposition of test data by manufacturers.

Table 5. 5: EU cold appliance policies – tests of effectiveness

Policy tool	Test of effectiveness	Evidence
Energy label	Has the legislation been implemented in member states?	Desk study
	Are labels on the appliances?	Survey in sample of shops
	Do consumers understand and (say they) use the label?	Consumer survey of people buying appliances
Minimum standard	Has the legislation been implemented in member states?	Desk study
	Have non-complying appliances been removed from sale?	Survey in sample of shops (only successful if all appliances are labelled correctly).
Energy label + min standard	Do declared values on appliances match values measured by independent test laboratories?	Testing of sample of appliances by independent laboratories
	How much energy has been saved / will be saved as a result of these policies (and others being pursued at the same time)?	Interpretation of detailed sales-weighted energy consumption data against historical background.

In some cases, even if good data are available, it is not possible to measure the energy saving effect of a policy in isolation, as a combination of policies has been introduced. For example, during recent years there have been various policy developments that might affect efficiency of cold appliances, including the phase out of CFCs, the introduction of energy labels, and the announcement of future minimum standards. Thus changes in the market are a combined reflection of all of these forces and other factors unrelated to government policy. However, the concentration of policies in the cold sector has resulted in projections of reduced energy consumption.

5.4.2 Predicting the effects of policy on energy consumption

The market for each product is different, as are the range of efficiency choices, which will affect the choice of policies and how they perform in each market. Therefore it is difficult to make generalisations about the likely effects of policy on energy consumption. For example, most refrigeration appliances are now only available with labels A to C, rather than full A to G; does this affect the effectiveness of the label?

Energy labels

Three years after the introduction of energy labels for cold appliances, the proportion labelled correctly in shops averaged 56% across the EU, varying from 17-94% in different member states (Winward *et al.*, 1998). It was shown that even in Denmark, where a high proportion of people said energy efficiency was important to them and 86% of appliances were labelled, only 56% of respondents said the label influenced their purchase. Based on this evidence, it cannot be assumed that labels will affect more than around 60% of decisions; other criteria and the choice available in the shops will limit consumer response.

Minimum standards / industry agreements

The most straightforward policy effect to estimate is that of the minimum standard since, assuming the standard is met (and this is quite a big assumption), the efficiency of new products is known on the introduction date. This information then has to be translated into energy consumption figures, which, for cold appliances, requires knowledge of the average size and type of appliance purchased. However, the question is then how efficiency will develop after imposition of the standard - whether the underlying rate of change will continue at the rate it would have done in the absence of the standard, or whether it will decrease. In previous work (DECADE, 1997a) different assumptions about manufacturer response to the introduction of minimum standards for cold appliances led to a range of expected savings in 2020 of 2% to 18%.

Information and advice

Information and advice about energy efficiency and fuel switching for consumers, retailers, installers and manufacturers is probably the policy tool whose effect is most difficult to predict. It is difficult even to define clear goals for this education, as it is part of a broader picture and a vital pre-cursor to enable responses to other policies (as demonstrated by the results of Winward *et al.*, above*)*.

Subsidies and rebates

In some schemes, the customer's old appliance is taken by the shop as a 'trade in' and thus removed from the second-hand market. It may be appropriate to count additional savings if this is the case. It is more difficult to estimate the indirect effects of subsidies. If subsides are acting to transform the market, they should be contributing to building the market for efficient appliances in general, and reducing the price of these appliances in future. Whether this is likely to be the case must involve a judgement of the state of the market, the scale of the scheme and whether it is large enough to have a market transformation effect.

5.5   ENERGY PRICES AND TAXES

One of the ways of making efficiency more economically attractive to consumers is to raise the price of energy via environmental taxes. In addition, a carbon-based energy tax could favour lower carbon fuels. Energy taxes are a blunt instrument compared with other market transformation policies. However, they may have a greater reach, as they can go beyond affecting purchase behaviour, and also affect usage. They also of course have the great advantage of raising revenue that could be used to finance other aspects of a market transformation strategy. Existing energy taxes in the UK and the Netherlands are described earlier (Sections 2.3.6 and 2.3.7).

The UK Department of Trade and Industry believes that electricity prices have little effect on domestic consumption, asserting that "electricity prices do not materially affect demand within the range of prices expected" (DTI, 1995). Although there is little evidence to show that consumers react to price increases in the short term, in the longer term there is an effect of higher energy prices encouraging greater energy efficiency (Boardman *et al.*, 1999). The longer term is at least five years, and longer with some products. In the long run, prices on energy will probably need to rise to meet environmental objectives. It is certainly important to give consumers the message that energy efficiency is desirable. Then, over time, they will be able to make lifestyle choices and purchasing decisions that will result in a lower level of energy use.

5.5.1   Carbon and energy tax

The European Commission has put forward a proposal for 'minimum excise duties'. The Commission is proposing that all energy products should be taxed and the rate for hydrocarbons updated. The proposal is to gradually increase the minimum duties on non-automotive energy carriers to 0.7 Euro/GJ in 2002. This duty would be the same for all final energy forms.

The proposal is currently stalled due to objections from Spain and Ireland. However, this proposal is seen as a potentially important contribution to meeting EU Kyoto obligations, and there have been recent suggestions that member states opposed to the tax could be allowed to opt out in the interest of securing an agreement (ENDS, 1999).

Taxes on energy to raise revenue have the advantage of creating an incentive to use less energy but they can be very regressive. This is of particular concern in the UK with its high prevalence of fuel poverty. The contrast between carbon taxes and market transformation policies as regards equity and low income households is shown below (Table 5. 6).

Table 5. 6: Taxes and market transformation – the equity dimension

	Taxes / pricing	Market transformation
Mechanism for encouraging efficiency	increases running costs	encourages efficient equipment purchases
Effect on low income households	regressive immediately	relatively harmful long-term
Remedy for low income households	income compensation	targeting of grants and subsidies

Although market transformation strategies can disadvantage lower income households in the longer term, as they do not have access to new appliances or the capital to buy them, energy or carbon taxes are immediately regressive, and it is hard to compensate for this effect. Nevertheless, the money for grants and subsidies offered under a market transformation programme has to come from somewhere, and in the end this may be carbon taxes. However, this would only be politically acceptable in the UK if the taxes could be implemented and grants distributed such that low income households did not suffer. The best circumstances would be to delay the imposition of taxes until the major variations in energy efficiency between households have been eliminated.

Suggested mechanism for introducing carbon taxes without affecting the poor
A possible mechanism by which a carbon tax could be introduced in the UK, without having a negative effect on low-income households, would be to transfer these households onto green electricity, which would not be subject to the tax. This proposal achieves a variety of objectives, not least increasing substantially the demand for renewable electricity in support of the government's target of 10% of all electricity to come from renewables by 2010. The consumption from this group of householders creates the demand on its own. This proposed scheme is called Green Electricity for Affordable Warmth (GEAW), for ease of identification.

With GEAW in place, additional policies could be implemented to create a monetary value for carbon emissions in the domestic sector. As low-income households are protected, a domestic carbon and energy tax can be introduced, that would be paid by better-off households only. The tax would be nearly three times higher on electricity than on gas, to reflect the relative carbon contents, and this reasoning would be clearly publicised. This should provide an incentive to better-off households to invest in energy efficient measures and to fuel switch. The revenue for the tax would be used, initially, to repay to the exchequer any premiums that were required for green electricity. The remaining balances would be used primarily to fund energy efficiency measures, such as those identified in the Kyoto+ Scenario.

The concept behind this scheme is the same as that being applied to non-domestic use through the UK Climate Change Levy for industry: green electricity users are exempt from the levy.

5.6 WIDER ISSUES

There are a number of different and competing selection criteria for deciding how to implement a market transformation or fuel-switching strategy:
- certainty of energy and carbon dioxide savings;
- equity;
- cost-effectiveness (for the regulated, for the government, for society).

The balance between these competing criteria may differ between countries to produce a policy suite which is socially and politically acceptable. For example, due to the importance of fuel poverty as an issue, equity may be more important in the UK than in the Netherlands and Portugal.

5.6.1 Certainty

Factors that increase certainty, both for governments (in terms of savings), and for manufacturers (in terms of the policy timetable) include:

- policies introduced by regulation;
- policies based on technology improvement and infrastructure change, rather than behavioural change;
- a firm timetable for introduction of future policies – EU framework legislation.

5.6.2 Equity

Although energy consumption has risen across the EU, it would be wrong to conclude that all households are now able to afford an adequate level of energy services. Fuel poverty, defined as the inability to provide adequate energy services for a home without spending at least 10% of household income (DTI, 1998; Boardman, 1991) is a serious concern in the UK and Ireland. In the UK, almost one third of households were considered to be in fuel poverty in 1996/97, the extreme consequence of which is thousands of additional winter deaths. The main causes are low income, energy inefficient housing and heating equipment, and living in oversized dwellings, and it is more likely to afflict small households, for example pensioners living alone and lone-parent families. Most other EU countries do not recognise fuel poverty as a social problem.

Equity can be included in a market transformation strategy, with no adverse effects on certainty. However, including equity will involve spending money on low-income households. Equity is an issue for member states in terms of the design of their rebate programmes. The concept of sustainability includes considerations of equity.

5.6.3 Cost-effectiveness

The technology standards suggested in Chapter 3 are economically justified from the point of view of the consumer. Therefore, by definition, all the measures included in ETP are at zero cost to the consumer, in fact the consumer will nearly always save money over the lifetime of the product as the ETP level has been set to the least life cycle cost, rather than the equivalent life cycle cost (see Glossary).

Despite this, manufacturers are not making, retailers are not stocking and consumers are not buying ETP technologies, and thus government expenditure in some form is needed to orient the market towards ETP and to transform the market. The question of cost-effectiveness is also one of time perspective. Policy expenditure may be short term, with savings (to consumers and society) accumulating over the long-term.

5.7 CONCLUSIONS

Market transformation is the current philosophy underlying much of EU and member state energy efficiency policy. This approach has a great deal to offer in delivering more efficient LAWH to consumers, and protects lower income consumers from the disadvantages of an energy or carbon tax. Market transformation policy instruments can be extended from energy efficiency to carbon efficiency in many cases. However, fuel switching raises policy issues which are outside the scope of current market transformation policy on energy efficient products.

New policies are being developed all the time, for instance those using the world-wide web and aggregated purchase. These, interestingly, extend the role of information provision in the market transformation strategy. The market works best with well-informed consumers and both these developments serve that function, as well as illuminating the strategies of their competitors for market players.

By improving the efficiency of new appliances purchased, real changes in energy consumption have been observed although, it is difficult to ascribe energy savings to specific policies because of other market developments, sales trends and social trends. Monitoring of the effects of policy is becoming a more important part of government thinking. Proper assessment of the effects of new policy demands both a very good understanding of the technical and policy environment and high quality data. In recent times, such analyses and data are becoming available, although they still have to be treated with some caution. In addition, the assessment needs to be seen as independent.

With the introduction of a competitive fuel – gas – into the assessments of carbon savings from LAWH, policy can no longer focus solely on the equipment: account has to be taken of the system, the household and even the availability of the fuel. This will be equally true when other fuel switching options are considered, for instance household-level renewables such as solar thermal and photovoltaics.

The variations across Europe in gas ownership and the carbon content of electricity mean that fuel-switching policy is country specific at present. This puts the onus onto the member states to develop their own policies on fuel-switching.

The policy agenda is becoming much broader, and many of the new dimensions of policy are national rather than EU concerns. The method of regulating the utilities may be as important as agreements with appliance manufacturers.

Labels for appliances where there are competing fuels is a problematic policy area. With the present diversity between member states, it is recommended that the labels for gas and electric appliances are separate and based on delivered energy. This will increase the importance of national policies on fuel priorities. As renewable energy products become more prevalent, the issue of labels will have to be revisited: how would gas, electric and solar water heaters be compared? The EU energy label may have to become the EU carbon label; this would fit with policies on car labels.

CHAPTER 6: POLICY SCENARIOS

Having outlined many different policy options and combinations in Chapter 5, the challenge is now to build these into coherent and credible policy scenarios. The aim of creating scenarios is to show carbon saving visions for the future that are backed by careful research and considered policy ideas. The carbon and energy savings under these scenarios are compared with both the reference case, and with the Kyoto commitments of all three member states.

Two scenarios will be presented. The first, the 'Kyoto+ Scenario', follows on from previous ECI work (DECADE, 1997b). The Kyoto+ Scenario (Section 6.1) combines both strong European and national policy commitments to energy efficiency and, now, to fuel switching. All four policy realms (see Figure 5. 1) are covered, to include policy on fuel choices.

The second is the 'Sustainability Scenario' (Section 6.2), under which deeper cuts in carbon emissions are required. The climate change imperative indicates that a more ambitious trajectory is needed if the long-term risks of climate change are to be avoided. This scenario goes beyond Kyoto+ and beyond the economic and technical potential identified in Chapter 3. The scenario debates the need for both greater technical change (whether or not it pays back to the consumer) and the extent to which broader, behavioural changes will be required. Market transformation, fiscal incentives and a strong educational and information strand to policy are all evident.

6.1   THE KYOTO+ SCENARIO

The Kyoto+ Scenario is based on the introduction of ETP technology. The key difference between Kyoto+ and the FS-ETP scenario is that the time scale for Kyoto+ is determined by the fastest realistic introduction of policies to ensure that ETP technology becomes the average on the market. For fuel switching, it is assumed that the same levels of network expansion is achieved as in FS-ETP.

6.1.1   Overview of savings

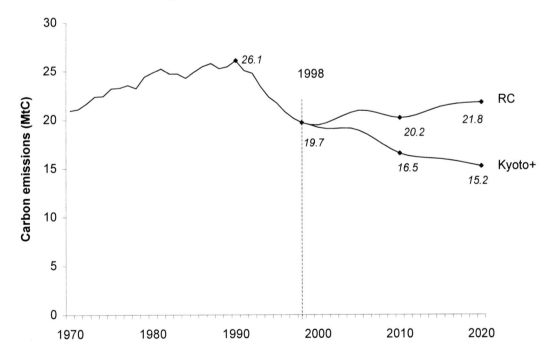

Figure 6. 1: Carbon emissions from gas and electric LAWH, UK, NL and PO combined, 1970 – 2020

Figure 6. 1 shows carbon emissions for the UK, Netherlands and Portugal combined in the reference case and Kyoto+ scenarios. Under Kyoto+ 18% savings compared with the reference case are made in 2010, and this increases to 30% by 2020.

Table 6. 1 shows energy consumption and carbon emissions for Kyoto+ in 2010 and 2020 and compares these with both the reference case and carbon savings expected under FS-ETP. Under Kyoto+ around 70% of the FS-ETP savings can be achieved by 2010 and almost 90% by 2020 as the effect of earlier introduction of ETP technology under FS-ETP diminishes.

Table 6. 1: Energy consumption, carbon emissions and savings, Kyoto+ Scenario

	UK		NL		PO	
	2010	2020	2010	2020	2010	2020
RC						
Electricity (TWh)	96.9	102.0	24.0	25.8	10.2	10.9
Gas (TWh)	68.4	67.6	18.8	19.5	9.3	8.9
Carbon (MtC)	14.0	15.8	4.2	4.2	1.9	1.8
Kyoto+						
Electricity (TWh)	74.3	62.0	17.8	15.4	7.3	5.5
Gas (TWh)	68.3	70.0	19.4	20.4	9.5	9.5
Carbon (MtC)	11.6	11.1	3.4	3.0	1.6	1.2
National savings (RC - Kyoto+)						
Electricity (TWh)	22.6	40.0	6.2	10.3	2.9	5.3
Gas (TWh)	0.08	-2.46	-0.61	-0.92	-0.20	-0.55
Carbon (MtC)	2.44	4.68	0.81	1.22	0.39	0.63
C savings as % of FS-ETP (%)	71	88	76	89	68	88

As in the FS-ETP scenario, fuel switching means that there is actually an increase in gas consumption in Kyoto+ (except for the UK in 2010). The Kyoto+ Scenario achieves carbon savings of 17.5%, 19.2% and 20% compared with RC in 2010 for the UK, Netherlands and Portugal respectively.

When compared with carbon emissions in 1990, the savings are 44% for the UK, 12.5% for the Netherlands and growth in emissions of 2.5% for Portugal. The large savings in the UK reflect the drop in carbon intensity of electricity since 1990, as explained in Chapter 3, and the growth in Portugal reflects the expected growth in energy demand. For all three countries, the savings are greater than the national Kyoto target for reduction of greenhouse gases from 1990 to 2010.

Comparison with previous UK scenario
In *2MtC*, savings of 2.7 MtC by 2010 were identified for the UK for electric lights and appliances. Using the same methodology and general approach as for the Kyoto+ Scenario, the equivalent figure for 2010 is now approximately 2 MtC (excluding savings due to LAWH which were not previously modelled). The major reason for this difference is that in the intervening two years, there has been less policy progress than expected; two years have effectively been 'lost'. This illustrates very powerfully how delays in the policy timetable compromise meeting the Kyoto targets.

6.1.2   General rules used in designing policy for the Kyoto+ Scenario
The Kyoto+ Scenario was constructed based on the following objectives, in order of importance:
- there is a high degree of certainty that the energy and carbon dioxide savings will be achieved if the policies are implemented;
- the cost to consumers is minimised;
- the importance of equity is recognised, to enable all income groups to participate.

To achieve certainty, as discussed in Chapter 5, all efficiency savings are underpinned by mandatory minimum standards. Industry agreements could, in theory, deliver the same savings (although it seems unlikely in practice due to high target levels) and this alternative mechanism may be preferred. The cost to consumers is minimised by either setting the efficiency level at today's best, or supporting more ambitious efficiency levels by programmes to ensure the cost of the technology will be economic by the time it is mandatory. The third objective means that many of the financial incentives for efficiency serve a dual purpose: both growing the market for energy efficient products and ensuring that the subsidised products are given to low-income households.

Ambitious efficiency targets are set for individual products, both in terms of the technology and the time scale within which this is achieved, in some cases the technology improvement goes beyond the ETP level. For example, under Kyoto+ electric tumble dryer technology is set at the best available, rather than ETP, thus achieving carbon emissions which are lower than those of the gas equivalent (see Table 3.9). Thus there are minimal additional carbon savings to be achieved by switching fuels for hobs, ovens and tumble dryers, given average EU electricity carbon intensity. However, considerable carbon savings can still be made by switching from electric to gas water heating, and by switching from LPG to natural gas appliances and water heating.

The time scale and sequence for actions at the EU level is based on experience of policy making to date, using the shortest realistic time scales (Table 6. 2). For some appliances, a longer period from announcement to introduction of the minimum standard has been allowed, this is because the minimum standard proposed entails new technology which could require major manufacturing changes.

Table 6. 2: Generic time scale for EU actions

Action	Time taken
Develop a new test procedure, including round-robin laboratory testing	2 years
Technology procurement, from study to competition winner	2 years
Study on labels and minimum standards, to recommend labelling scheme and standard level. Introduce labels and announce minimum standard.	2 years from introduction of test procedure
Minimum standard announced, based on technology demonstrated via technology procurement and subsequent market-building policies	2 years from technology procurement competition winner
Minimum standard in place	4 years after announcement of minimum standard

6.1.3 EU policy timetables for efficiency

An outline policy timetable for appliances and water heating in the Kyoto+ Scenario is presented, and this is the basis on which savings from Kyoto+ have been calculated (Table 6. 3). This timetable is necessarily summarised and does not include starting dates for the studies that would be needed to support these policies, nor the dates on which the policies should be announced. These can be derived from the rules given in Table 6. 2. Neither does it include the national policies that would be required in support of EU actions (Section 6.1.4).

It is striking that a number of the ETP levels can be introduced just as quickly as in the ETP2005 scenario (in which all new appliances in 2005 are at ETP). This is because, in several cases, the ETP technology e.g. washing machines and dishwashers is already available on the market, and by 2005 it is expected that all manufacturers will be able to produce it at a price which pays back to the consumer. More technologically ambitious ETP levels (particularly for cold appliances) will take longer to introduce.

Two example timetables are given in detail for the sectors from which the largest savings are expected, cold appliances and lighting, to show all the stages in a policy programme. Timetables for all appliance groups can be found in Appendix T.

Table 6. 3: Year of introduction of EU policy measures for LAWH in the Kyoto+ Scenario

Appliance	Test procedure	Technology procurement	Label	Minimum standard / corporate average efficiency
All				2000 – framework directive for minimum standard
Cold		2002-2004 for ETP technology	2002 – first revision 2006 – second revision 2010 – third revision	2007- intermediate 2010 – ETP
Consumer electronics				
TV	2002 on-mode	2000-2002 for low energy screens, beyond ETP	2004 on-mode	2005 ETP standby 2008 ETP on-mode
VCR, audio, RD, transformers & power supply units				2005 ETP standby
Cooking				
Electric ovens				2004 ETP
Gas ovens	2002		2002	2006 – reference case
Electric hobs	2001		2004	2008 ETP
Lighting				2000-2010 corporate average bulb efficiency
Water heating				
Gas boilers			2002	2004 corporate average boiler efficiency
DESWH			2002	2006 ETP
Wet appliances				
Washing machines	2001-revisions	2000 for intelligent hot fill, beyond ETP	2004 – first revision	2004 ETP
Electric tumble dryer				2007 heat-pump standard
Dishwasher				2004 ETP

Cold appliances

Two rounds of energy labels, procurement, subsidy and minimum standards will be necessary to enable the minimum standard introduced in 2010 to be the ETP level. These standards have been labelled A+ (approximate efficiency index = 0.42) and A++ (approximate efficiency index = 0.2). Programmes to increase the market share of efficient appliances are likely to be largely implemented at a national level, although EU-wide aggregated purchase will also contribute (known as Energy+, see Section 5.2.2).

Table 6. 4: Policy timetable for the Kyoto+ Scenario, cold appliances

Current status	Labels implemented 1.1.95 Standards agreed in 1996 (96/57/EC), implemented 1999 Preparatory study on new label
2000	Aggregated purchase for A+ (EI = 0.42) – already underway Energy+
2001	Programmes to increase penetration of A+ to 10-20% new sales
2002	1st revision of label introduced Announce 2nd round of standards requiring efficiency index of 0.42 A++ technology procurement study and competition (EI of 0.2)
2004	A ++ procurement winner launched Programmes to increase penetration of A++ to 5% of new sales
2005	Programmes to increase penetration of A++ to 10-20% new sales
2006	2nd round of standards becomes mandatory (A+) 2nd revision to label Announce 3rd round of standards
2010	3rd round of standards implemented, all appliances ETP (A++) 3rd revision to label

Lighting

Of all appliance groups, accessing the ETP levels of CFL requires the greatest changes, and is the most challenging in policy terms.

A minimum standard, which removed incandescent bulbs from the market, is very unlikely to be acceptable. As an alternative, a Corporate Average Bulb Efficiency is suggested (Table 6. 5). The average bulb efficiency would be set to increase over time, to ensure increasing production of CFLs without necessarily outlawing any particular type of bulb. This policy instrument provides some flexibility in shifting the majority of sales from incandescent bulbs to CFLs. Nevertheless, it would still involve major changes in the structure of the bulb manufacturing industry, and it is anticipated a ten-year period would be the minimum necessary to approach ETP levels of CFL ownership.

Table 6. 5: Policy timetable for the Kyoto+ Scenario, lighting

Current Status	Voluntary agreement to phase out magnetic ballasts by 2008 Energy label to be introduced from 1.1.2001 European design competition on dedicated fittings
2000	5 year national programmes begin to install 2 CFLs in every household Mandatory 10 year targets for Corporate Average Bulb Efficiency (CABE), including agreements on luminaires with integral ballasts R and D support on new control technologies to overcome technical barriers to CFLs
2001	5 year programme begins to install 2 dedicated CFL fittings in every household
2002	Begin 15 year programme to retrofit 8 million targeted households (UK)
2003	Two integral ballast luminaires included in new homes through Building Regulations
2005	2 bulbs in every household achieved as a direct result of national action UK target total market for CFLs of 24.5 million bulbs pa, to be maintained by CABE agreements
2006	2 dedicated fittings in every household achieved as a direct result of national actions
2007	Integral ballast luminaires included as part of building standards.

To encourage consumers to embrace this technology switch, the objective for national governments is to get one or two CFLs into every house, so that people have the opportunity to test the light source for themselves. Research shows that householders are generally satisfied with the new technology and buy additional CFLs (DELight, 1997). In the longer term, savings are achieved through the installation of fittings that will only take CFLs, so there is no chance of the householder reverting to the old, incandescent bulbs that use more energy.

Discussion

The Kyoto+ Scenario has been designed to be achievable; it follows the usual path of EU policy and is timed in accordance with experience of best practice to date. Nevertheless, to achieve Kyoto+ would require significant policy action for almost every appliance group in 2000, whether introducing a framework directive on minimum standards, or setting up a study on electric hobs. This is rather ambitious, given the current resources allocated to energy efficiency policy at EU level. In addition, strong political commitment would be required to meet this timetable, and previous experience shows it may not be forthcoming. Therefore, the following section (about the role of the member states) considers both policy that would be required if the Kyoto+ EU policy timetable were met, and the additional national policy that could compensate if it were delayed.

6.1.4   National policy in support of EU policy for Kyoto+

The role played by member states in a market transformation strategy to date has been mainly focused on building the market for efficient technologies. As outlined in Chapter 5, this includes educating and informing consumers and other actors about efficiency and environment issues and providing economic incentives to increase sales of efficient products. However, with the introduction of fuel switching, the role of the member state is expanded, as much of this policy will be developed at member state level. In addition, to ensure the Kyoto+ savings are made, member states can also expand their traditional energy efficiency policy role in order to further support and enhance EU policy.

Promoting efficiency
Different methods of reducing the price of efficiency (subsidies, altered VAT, aggregate purchase and increased price competition) were discussed in detail in Chapter 5. Some or all of these methods should be used by national governments to increase the market share of the most efficient appliances, in support of the EU policy above. In the absence of sufficiently strong minimum standards being introduced by the EU, member states would need to undertake more ambitious campaigns using these tools in order to increase the efficiency of the average appliance sold.

Further, member states could promote higher efficiency standards for electrical equipment, but this is difficult for individual countries. However, it is being achieved by the eight countries in the Group for Efficient Appliances (GEA), on a voluntary basis. This currently includes the Netherlands, but not the UK or Portugal. Should the Commission be unwilling or unable to implement sufficiently challenging minimum standards, the role of GEA could be enhanced to undertake some of this work.

Policy on country specific appliances
Where appliances are only of importance in a limited number of EU countries, national rather than EU policy is likely to be the appropriate route to energy savings. Both hot water storage cylinders and kettles are peculiar to the UK and Ireland; ownership levels are very low in most of the rest of Europe (although there is some use of storage cylinders in the Netherlands). Thus there is unlikely to be interest in, or reason for, policy-making at an EU level. Delivery of efficiency savings for these products in the UK will thus rely on UK-only action. A policy for kettles would include a design competition, an endorsement label of more efficient products, and subsidies to reduce extra cost of insulated kettles (see Appendix T for full details). No important country specific appliances were identified for either Portugal or the Netherlands.

Supporting fuel switching
For Portugal and the UK, one of the key fuel switching policies which must be adopted by the national government is to accelerate the expansion of the gas network. The rate of expansion of the UK gas network which was described in Chapter 3 (90% of households to be connected by 2010) is achievable. Two alternative policy routes are suggested to meet this goal. Firstly, the Government or Regulator could require Transco (the company in charge of the gas network) to extend the gas network via the Utilities Bill, for instance as an environmental objective. Alternatively, it may be possible to alter the pricing formula and place greater emphasis on the number of customers, rather than on the amount of gas sold. This would provide Transco with a financial incentive to extend the network, and would require the support of the Regulator. The mechanism chosen in Portugal will depend on national circumstances.

As suggested in Chapter 5, use of gas could also be consolidated by requiring that all new homes within the gas network have gas space and water heating installed with additional connection points for other gas appliances. However, in the UK and Portugal, much expansion of the gas network will be into areas of existing housing, where compulsory connection does not seem a realistic policy option. Based on existing patterns of adoption for the UK, it is assumed that if the gas network is expanded, little in the way of incentives will be needed to persuade people to connect for space and water heating. Utilities in Portugal have developed successful strategies to persuade consumers to switch from LPG to natural gas. Incentives may be necessary in order to persuade them to also connect for gas hobs, ovens and tumble dryers. As shown in Chapter 4, simply offering a financial incentive may not be sufficient to encourage or enable consumers to choose gas.

Member states will have to promote the debate about fuel switching at a national level. As well as general advice and information, this could include, for instance, in the UK putting the Energy Saving Trust's energy efficiency logo on gas appliances, rather than electrical ones (e.g., gas hobs, not radiant electric hobs). Similarly, existing investment funds such as those supporting housing improvements could be channelled towards efficient gas appliances, rather than electrical ones, where there is a fuel choice. However, the priorities of the individual programmes might not combine well with those of reducing carbon emissions.

Creating a carbon market
As discussed in Chapter 5, creating a carbon market could be a powerful way of bringing together energy efficiency, renewable energy and fuel switching policies. Focussing on carbon reductions could help governments clarify the links between these sometimes disparate policy areas, and enable considerable carbon savings to be made regardless of EU (in)action. In addition, informing consumers (and other actors) about their carbon impact empowers them to choose lower carbon futures for themselves.

Creating a carbon market involves actors other than simply consumers. The proposal suggested here is called average utility carbon per household, or AUCH. National governments would set sector targets for carbon reductions, and based on this would give utilities a reducing cap for carbon emissions. Initial allocation of emissions permits to the utilities would be based on the number of customers, with separate allocations for gas and electricity use. From the government point of view, the great advantage of this scheme is that by setting carbon reduction targets so directly, it can be sure they will be achieved.

The utility will achieve lower average household carbon emissions through the investment in both lower carbon technologies (including renewable energy) and in reducing demand per household. The utility can encourage fuel switching by their customers, particularly if it is a dual-fuel utility, but this is not the only option available. The extent to which higher energy services will be available to consumers will depend upon improvements in energy efficiency and the use of fuel switching options. One of the interesting implications of AUCH is that the energy companies would have a strong interest in ensuring that appliances become more efficient, as this helps to reduce the annual carbon emissions per household. Discussions on industry agreements in Brussels would no longer be a debate between government and the appropriate trade association. The utilities would be alongside the government representatives trying to persuade the manufacturing industries to be more ambitious in their efficiency targets.

Developing a carbon market for domestic consumers is, at least initially, also about awareness and education. The majority of private individuals in the UK do not realise that their activities result in carbon dioxide releases, or that these are the primary cause of climate change. There are other policy initiatives occurring that will create this awareness, for instance, the EU is requiring carbon dioxide emission levels to be shown on the energy labels for cars, mandatory from the end of 2000. A wider approach to education on emissions is timely and appropriate, and would be doubly effective if occurring in two household-related energy use sectors concurrently.

There are various ways in which this information could be provided to the householder, but the simplest way would be for fuel bills to include carbon dioxide emissions, and for this to be compared to the average level for similar households. Research would be required as to whether the information should be on the normal quarterly bill, whether there is an annual total, how to combine different fuels and what form of comparison would be most appropriate. As illustrated in Chapter 5, this type of approach for energy savings has been shown to have significant results. In Portugal this method of information provision would not work for bottled LPG, an alternative mechanism would need to be found.

Having provided information on consumption and emissions to consumers via energy bills, further information could be provided via a carbon audit of the home, so that all properties were graded in terms of carbon emissions. This would ensure that household emission levels had an importance and status and can be built into other policy initiatives. The eventual aim would be to have a formal ranking system, such as existing household energy audit systems, so that properties and households could be graded from highest to lowest levels of carbon emissions. As householders become carbon aware, they can make across-fuel decisions for themselves.

Increased information to consumers and AUCH can be combined, so that both householders and utilities are moving towards the common goal of reducing carbon emissions. There is a strong logic in involving both energy users and suppliers in the climate change targets, through using the same method of measurement – carbon. If the duty is placed on only one of the players, then the actions of the other could offset any progress made in carbon conservation. The importance of involving 'hearts and minds' is discussed further in the Sustainability Scenario.

Discussion

If the EU fails to meet the timetable in the Kyoto+ Scenario, not only will member states need to increase energy efficiency on a national level, they will also have to engage more fully with household-level fuel switching. This is because without very strong electrical efficiency targets, more significant carbon advantages from switching fuels from electricity to gas will be available.

6.1.5 Costs of the programme

The method of identifying technology improvements in the Kyoto+ Scenario and ETP is in line with the European methodology used in preliminary studies prior to the introduction of minimum standards and voluntary agreements. This entails setting technology standards which will pay back to the consumer even though all the additional costs to manufacturers are assumed to be passed on to the consumer. If costs to the manufacturer and consumer were both estimated and included, there would be double-counting. As the ETP is actually set at least life cycle cost, the Kyoto+ Scenario will result in net financial savings to individual consumers and to society.

The majority of the EU policy programme is assumed to be at fairly minor cost: the costs of legislating, negotiating standards, designing test procedures etc. are part of the normal EU functions. The parts of the Kyoto+ policy package to which costs can be explicitly attached are the technology procurement and subsidy programmes. Technology procurement costs will be at the EU level, whereas the costs of subsidies (and other policies for reducing the price of efficiency) will fall at a national level. These are the most expensive part of any policy package and it is very much in the member states' interests to achieve as much of Kyoto+ as possible via (cheaper) EU actions. If EU policy action is not strong enough to achieve efficiency savings via minimum standards, the cost implications to member states of achieving the savings by other means could be very significant.

Delivering equity in the UK

Equity is not identified as an important dimension of energy policy in the Netherlands or Portugal, therefore this discussion relates specifically to the UK. As noted in Chapter 5, equity can be included in a market transformation strategy, with no adverse effects on certainty. However, including equity will involve spending money on low-income households. In the UK, the utilities are obliged to invest in energy efficiency in the domestic sector, through Standards of Performance (SOP). At least two-thirds of this money has to be spent on disadvantaged consumers – in this context defined as the poor, disabled and pensioners. This definition includes, therefore, non-poor households. The combined annual expenditure on lights, appliances and water heating is just over 37.5m Euros, with over half going on lights (EST, 1999). There are, therefore, some useful sums of money going in to develop the efficiency of these markets, particularly to benefit the poor.

Funding for both SOP and HEES (see Glossary) will probably be larger in future years. It is assumed that from 2003 and until 2011, the funding of SOP (known as SOP 4) will increase by a factor of five, although this may be optimistic. Two programmes are illustrated below to give an indication of the scale of the programmes anticipated under current and expected future funding (Table 6. 6). These are compared with the scale of programmes suggested as necessary in *2MtC*.

The expected increase in SOP 4 would provide the necessary CFLs, but only a few of the dedicated fittings suggested in *2MtC*. Hence, SOP 4 (together with HEES) might
- enable the remaining low-income households to obtain 2 free CFLs each, over the five years to 2007;
- start to distribute dedicated light fittings, but to only a tiny fraction of low-income households, so that the market develops slowly.

With cold appliances, there is a considerable difference between the scale of programme required to either subsidise 20% of new appliances per year as suggested in *2MtC* (approximately 600,000 cold appliances) and the scale of existing and anticipated programmes.

Therefore, the present schemes and their likely successors are providing an equity dimension, but are:
- too small;
- targeted on the disadvantaged, which includes pensioners, whether rich or poor;
- for cold appliances, not promoting the most efficient new technology.

Either further funding will have to be found to allow equity to be delivered in tandem with market transformation goals, or methods other than subsidies will be required to deliver the equity dimension.

Table 6. 6: Annual programmes aimed at the disadvantaged, current and projected, UK

	Households per annum	Cost per annum (£m / Euros m)
CFLs (£4 / 6 Euros each)		
CFLs - SOP 3 and HEES - 2 CFLs each 2000-2002.	1,120,000	4.5 / 6.75
Lighting – SOP 4 and HEES – 2002 onwards, assumed at 5 x SOP 3, but divided between CFLs 2 bulbs for 20% of households	4,800,000	19.2 / 28.8
Dedicated fittings, two per household	55,000	3.3 / 4.95
Cold appliances (£100 / 150 Euros each)		
Fridgesavers through SOP 3 2000-2002.	40,000	4 / 6
Fridgesavers - 2002 onwards, SOP 4	200,000	20 / 30

6.2   SUSTAINABILITY SCENARIO

The Kyoto+ Scenario is based on technology improvement and fuel switching. The consumer is involved in making these changes, but they do not involve any changes to consumer lifestyle, behaviour or standards of service. As identified in Chapter 2, the major drivers of increased energy usage are the increasing number of households and increased ownership and usage of energy using equipment. The question is whether sustainable energy consumption can be achieved without tackling these more difficult and politically sensitive issues.

To investigate this, a definition of sustainable energy consumption is derived (Section 6.2.1), and the savings which would be required are compared with those available via the Kyoto+ Scenario. Section 6.3.2 discusses forms of behavioural changes that can promote the sustainable use of LAWH. Section 6.3.3 considers 'packages' of behavioural change and draws conclusions. The purpose of the Sustainability Scenario is to show the gap between what can be achieved with technology improvements and switching to gas, and what is required, and to discuss possible methods of filling that gap. The policy packages suggested have not been modelled in the way the effects of policy were modelled for the Kyoto+ Scenario, and all the figures quoted should be treated as approximate. Where figures are given, they are based on the UK as an example, but the principles and ideas are relevant for all three countries.

6.2.1   Sustainable carbon emissions
Sustainable energy use involves:
1. reducing greenhouse gas concentrations to a level that will not cause longer-term global temperatures to rise unacceptably, and
2. sharing 'permission' to emit greenhouse gases fairly between nations.

Various organisations have suggested sustainability targets for energy, including the Global Commons Institute, Friends of the Earth and the European Environment Agency (Figure 6. 2). To compare these with the results of this project, an indication of sustainable levels of carbon emissions for 2020 is required. Using these figures, to achieve 'true' world sustainability (0.2tC/person/year) by 2100, UK carbon emissions in 2020 need to be approximately1.6tC/person/year. An intermediate world target of 1tC per person is set for 2030 to aid contraction and convergence of countries

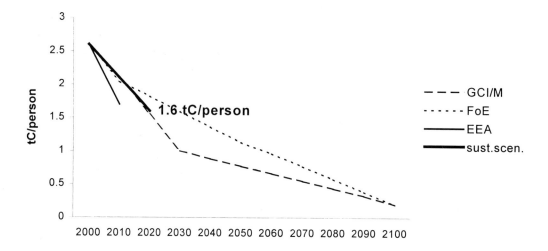

Figure 6. 2: **UK carbon emissions (tC/person/year) to achieve sustainability in 2100**

Source: McLaren *et al.*, (1998); Global Commons Institute (1999); European Environment Agency (1999)

For the UK, this means reducing total emissions to 99.5MtC in 2020, compared with 1998's 154MtC, i.e., a 35% reduction. These reductions will have to be achieved across all sectors, not just domestic LAWH. However, there is likely to be severe difficulty in achieving any savings at all from the transport sector, whose emissions currently show strong growth, and are expected to continue to rise by 2020 (DETR, 1997). Assuming transport emissions could be stabilised at 1998 levels, other sectors would need to reduce their carbon emissions by 43% by 2020 to reach sustainability (if transport emissions grow as projected, 63% reductions from other sectors would be required). Clearly, further savings will be required beyond 2020 to keep moving towards the target of 0.2tC per capita in 2100.

The Kyoto+ Scenario, if implemented in full and on time, would deliver 17% carbon savings by 2020 compared with emissions in 1998. This is much less than the 43% identified above: considerable further action is needed to move towards sustainability. Achieving the Sustainability Scenario will require people to change their behaviour: not only how they buy, use and dispose of their LAWH, but also how they live, work and travel. In many cases, consumer responsibility will go hand in hand with improved quality of life - lower bills, greater choice, better health – so individuals could, given enough information and a rational approach to decision-making, voluntarily change their behaviour to reduce their carbon emissions. In other cases, consumer responsibility reduces individuals' amenity but benefits the environment and wider society: such measures would require potentially unpopular regulation and enforcement.

6.2.2   Ownership levels and usage

This section considers a wide range of measures to promote behavioural change. It focuses on changing appliance ownership and use: aspects of LAWH emissions not challenged in previous chapters. Some of the proposed policies may be socially or politically unrealistic at present, and are intended to promote discussion rather than act as policy recommendations.

Traditional economics are based on the principle of non-saturation, which assumes that human needs are infinite, needs are reflected as economic demands, and meeting economic demands will meet needs (Sachs *et al.*, 1998). In terms of LAWH, this suggests ever-increasing levels of ownership and usage. Although increasing levels of efficiency can counterbalance some of the energy requirements of these appliances, the potential for improved efficiency is limited. Reduced ownership and usage, a form of voluntarily constrained consumption, must play a part in reducing energy use. A number of approaches to these reductions are discussed below

Design appliances to give information and change behaviour

In previous work (DECADE, 1997) it was demonstrated that the potential exists for electricity savings of almost 12% from UK domestic lights and appliances, by consumers making changes to the way they use their appliances without having to accept reduced service or incurring additional expenditure. However, beyond education campaigns, whose effect is uncertain and long-term, no mechanisms were identified to secure these savings.

It is now suggested that appliances themselves could provide better information and feedback to consumers. Current appliances give little information on how householders can be eco-friendly, or use their appliances in a less wasteful manner. Appliances that were designed to give more feedback, could themselves help to change behaviour. Some illustrations of this idea are given below:

- new houses could come with (low energy) intelligent metering, that explains where the energy comes from, and how much energy is being used and carbon emitted;
- 'Informative bills' which facilitate significant domestic energy savings (see Chapter 3). Even a 5% reduction in UK domestic energy use would lead to a 1.8MtC reduction (for all household energy, including space heating);
- wet appliances could include sensors which tell the consumer by how much loads could be increased, and suitable water and detergent levels for the load. Some appliances are already approaching this level of sophistication;
- ovens and electric kettles could be fitted with displays that shows the temperature inside, to avoid unnecessary re-heating or over-long warm-up times.
- appliances on standby could switch off unless the consumer over-rides the automatic switch-off, or, more radically, stand-by settings on all appliances could be abolished.

Distinguish between ownership, use and service

Traditionally, appliance use has been linked to ownership: to use an appliance we generally need to own it. Many people thus own appliances that they only use a few times per year, and over-large appliances (and houses) to cater for the occasional party or overnight guest (Wilhite and Lutzenhiser, 1997). Reducing individual ownership of appliances, for instance through rental schemes, may not reduce appliance use, but does mean that fewer appliances need to be produced, with fewer environmental impacts.

More importantly for this study, energy efficiency improvements can be more easily taken up where the consumer is supplied with a service and does not own the appliance. For instance, Electrolux is piloting a SAVE funded 'pay as you use' scheme for white goods using very efficient appliances, which will be replaced more frequently than usual to ensure the consumer always has access to highly efficient appliances. This sort of approach changes the economics of appliance purchase and usage, and may encourage the consumer to pay for a service which is delivered by a technology that more closely matches the ETP or least life cycle cost.

Green consumerism

Going beyond the idea of changing peoples' behaviour through their purchases is that of 'green consumerism': getting people to actively purchase products based on their eco-friendliness. Promoting green consumerism puts emphasis on providing suitable information to consumers to enable them to make the appropriate choice. Current market transformation policy approaches effectively expect consumers to behave in this way, by using the energy label to make efficient choices. A greater emphasis on the role of the consumer would tend to lead to policies such as:

- energy labels on a wider range of appliances;
- labels that encourage energy conservation and downsizing, rather than energy efficiency;
- promoting green electricity.

However, green consumerism is still a form of consumerism, albeit one where satisfaction comes partly from a reduced environmental impact.

Voluntary simplicity

The most eco-friendly form of behavioural change involves doing without, as a form of self-imposed constraint: "nothing is as efficient as appliances which are not purchased" (Sachs *et al.*, 1998). Voluntary simplicity, or down-shifting, does not necessarily mean a reduced quality of life – the people who make these choices do so because they believe it will enhance their lives. Nørgård (1996) suggests that, if "lifestyle efficiency" equals satisfaction/(energy service) consumption, then the efficiency of Western lifestyles is declining to the point where consumption may no longer increase satisfaction at all. For instance, a new appliance could ostensibly increase utility, but the owner may not have enough time to enjoy it, or its use could mean less use of other appliances. We are still far from any widespread acceptance of the need to reduce personal consumption, much less public willingness to do so. However the debate has started about the difference between quality of life and standard of living: more does not necessarily mean better.

Fundamentally this way of thinking may need to become widespread if sustainable energy use (particularly in the longer term) is to be achieved. Appropriate policy on energy use and carbon emissions would only have a small part to play in the social revolution which would be needed to achieve voluntary acceptance of reduced consumption levels.

6.2.3 Further fuel switching options

There is a wider dimension to fuel switching: the choice could be for renewable energy rather than fossil-fuel based consumption. For instance, the switch could be to solar water heaters on the roof. These have not been modelled in either of the scenarios, but are patently opportunities for reducing carbon dioxide emissions (see Section 3.5.5). Their adoption may depend upon the value placed on carbon saving – a rebate to replace electric with solar water heating would save more carbon than if the displaced fuel is gas. These household-level renewable energy sources need to be supported through a market transformation approach, just as efficient appliances are being, and by the development of the domestic carbon market.

6.2.4 Household size

Energy use would not increase if households stayed larger, as shown in Chapter 2. If the UK population in 2020 lived in households of 2.6 rather than 2.2 (as expected) people, then domestic electricity use would go down by more than 8%, gas use by more than 7%, and carbon emissions by roughly 2.8MtC in comparison with total domestic energy consumption (including space heating). Halting and possibly reversing the decline in household size would be a very significant contribution to energy saving. However, as discussed previously, the change in household size is based on underlying social trends that are completely outside the realm of energy policy. Indeed, it is unclear that any government policy would be effective in affecting these trends to any significant extent. Nevertheless a few ideas are discussed below.

Financial instruments could be used to encourage social trends towards different forms of households. Currently about 1% of English households take in at least one lodger (Office for National Statistics, 1998), this could be further encouraged by allowing more tax-free income for people who let out rooms in their house. Another possibility would be to provide tax breaks for mortgages shared by two people, and to make it easier for unrelated individuals to buy homes together. Both of these policies could help restrain demand for additional properties, which of course have environmental effects beyond the energy use of the inhabitants.

Alternatively, if it proves impossible to encourage people to live in larger groups, governments could focus on policy to provide housing which is appropriately sized for these smaller households, particularly for one-person households. As discussed in Chapter 2, more research is needed to determine how large the energy savings from this sort of policy might be.

6.2.5 Possible packages of behavioural change measures

The previous section has suggested a range of policy measures, which can each help to reduce carbon emissions through behavioural change. Further emissions can be saved through the increased use of renewables, CHP, fuel cells etc.

However most of these measures cannot be applied in isolation, and need to be buttressed with complementary measures. Four illustrative packages of measures are presented at Box 6.1. The calculations of savings are approximate, and are for the UK. Similar percentage savings would apply to the Netherlands and Portugal. The carbon saved through the packages does not include efficiency and fuel-switching improvements already calculated in Kyoto+. The savings from the packages cannot be added directly to efficiency savings or to each other, since improvements in one will reduce the savings in the other.

Box 6.1 Packages of measures for behavioural change

Package 1 – behavioural change through information and consumer choice/support (possible savings up to 1.5MtC, plus savings from renewables)
Legislation to support formation of ESCOs and require wider use of energy labels ➜ energy labels on wider range of appliances ➜ identify/promote/procure appliances that give feedback ➜ informative bills ➜ ESCOs promote energy-saving measures, incl. package of information to consumers about how they can reduce bills ➜ PV/solar hot water heating

Package 2 – behavioural change through service functions (savings uncertain)
Increase choice of service functions: laundry, cooking, heating ➜ 10% households buy smaller ovens, fridges, freezers, and 10% give up their ovens, washing machines, tumble dryers, but functions still need to be provided centrally, plus transport to get them to peoples' homes

Package 3 – behavioural change by building different homes (possible savings up to 0.7MtC, plus savings from renewables, plus effect on transport and community life)
Strengthen Building Regulations ➜ tax incentives for people renting rooms and buying houses together ➜ stop energy use in unoccupied homes ➜ energy audits of all houses at time of sale ➜ subsidise pilot housing communities with smaller houses but communal facilities ➜ communal renewable energy production

Package 4 – behavioural change through voluntary simplicity (possible savings 0.3MtC, plus savings from renewables, plus effect on travel behaviour and community life)
Tax incentives for people renting rooms or buying houses together ➜ make choice of shorter work weeks mandatory ➜ form "simplicity circles" including advice on reduced appliance use ➜ set up "tool libraries", car share clubs, house share/exchange clubs, solar clubs ➜ people give up non-essential appliances as they break down ➜ solar water heating/PV through clubs

---

However, even by adding together packages 1 – 4 and Kyoto+ (and hence overestimating potential savings) the savings achieved represent only a 36% reduction on 1998 carbon emission levels, i.e. not sufficient to reach the easier sustainability target of a 43% reduction. This highlights the necessity of achieving savings from renewable energy, both on the supply side and at a household level if carbon emissions from the domestic sector are to approach sustainable levels.

In sum, the Kyoto+ Scenario will not achieve, by 2020, the reductions in carbon emissions needed to achieve sustainability by 2100. To do so requires behavioural change. Some of this can be encouraged through policy changes, particularly provision of information and feedback to consumers. However, much will involve individuals changing their lifestyles as a form of consumer responsibility in a global carbon market. Voluntary behavioural changes can often be encouraged through policies that both increase people's quality of life and reduce carbon emissions, but stronger and currently less popular measures may also become acceptable. However, even the changes in behaviour envisaged in packages 1 – 4 will not be sufficient to approach sustainability; renewable energy options (some of which were discussed in Chapter 3) will also need to be in place.

6.3   CONCLUSIONS

Considerable carbon savings can be delivered via the policy programme outlined in the Kyoto+ Scenario, an average of 18% of the reference case in 2010 and 30% by 2020. However, in order for Kyoto+ to become a reality there would need to be strong political support at an EU and member state level for reducing carbon dioxide emissions, procurement and rebate programmes at the national level underpinned by EU-wide efficiency standards. Based on past performance, this strong EU action may not be forthcoming quickly enough.

In the absence of strong EU action, member states could ensure they still achieved significant carbon savings by increasing the efficiency appliances sold in their own markets, and by encouraging further fuel switching. However, it will be more difficult to ensure that the same degree of savings are made, since the majority of savings are available from strong action on efficiency, action which is difficult to take at member state level. In addition, without the underpinning of minimum standards the certainty of savings is also harder to achieve.

A national approach which could deliver guaranteed savings would be the introduction of carbon budgets for utilities. The utilities would have to ensure reducing carbon emissions by a combination of efficiency and fuel switching measures both in supply and through changing demand. To reinforce this approach, consumers would also be made aware of the impact of their own energy use in carbon terms: the 'carbon market' would be brought down to the level of the household. Increasing consumer education and awareness of energy and carbon issues is key to the success of many policies, whether within a carbon market framework or not.

Consensus definitions of sustainable carbon emissions, however, show that even the savings under the Kyoto+ Scenario will not be sufficient to put the UK, Netherlands and Portugal firmly on the path to sustainability. In order to achieve greater savings, other policy approaches including better information to consumers, change of behaviour and increasing the uptake of household level renewable energy systems will be required. In the Sustainability Scenario the key importance of public engagement with the aim of reducing carbon emissions comes even more clearly into focus. Although improved technology can deliver the first steps towards sustainability, it can not guarantee sufficient savings on its own.

CHAPTER 7: IMPLICATIONS FOR THE EU

The lessons gained from detailed examination of the three study countries can be applied to the other 12 EU member states to give a European overview. In order to do this it is first necessary to outline the uses of gas and electricity in the domestic sectors in each country, the gas network in each country, and the carbon intensity of electricity. Once that has been done, a simple set of calculations can be carried out to give rough estimates of carbon savings across the whole EU under the Kyoto+ Scenario.

Other EU countries have not been modelled as the UK, Netherlands and Portugal have, as this was outside of the scope of the project. However, to gain an understanding of the domestic energy consumption in the other countries the current project collected relevant information - the Country Pictures, which are summarised in this chapter. The research behind the CADENCE Country Pictures (published in full in a separate document) is an attempt to understand the ways in which households in different member states consume energy. Are there differences? What are the reasons? What are the implications for EU-wide policy?

This work aims to develop an overall picture of EU domestic energy consumption, which contributes to and complements the main modelling work. It provides a background against which the suitability and/or the feasibility of potential EU policy instruments may be assessed. In this overview the main findings of the research are presented, along with attempts to place domestic consumption into an infrastructural, social and cultural context. Despite the summary analysis of the individual uses and countries, there is sufficient detail to give the magnitude of the potential total savings.

7.1   CURRENT EU ENERGY USE PATTERNS

In 1996, total energy consumption by the EU residential sector was 2,861 TWh (IEA/OECD, 1998b), with natural gas accounting for 41% and electricity for 21% of the total. The remaining energy sources are oil (23%), coal (3%) and other (12%) which includes renewables and district heating.

There is no robust EU reference case of end-use. However, a number of end-use studies have been carried out at the EU-level, which can be used to disaggregate the consumption in the EU domestic sector. Table 7.1 shows the estimated consumption by end-use, which are based on data from these studies, listed as the source. Consumption by space heating and cooling is not covered here, in parallel with the rest of the report.

Table 7.1 EU domestic energy consumption by end-use

		RC, 1998 Delivered Energy (TWh)	Source
ELECTRIC	CE (less misc standby)	72	Estimate
	CE - Misc standby	20	Molinder (1997)
	Cold	109	Waide (1999)
	Cooking	51	National data derived
	Lighting	89	DELight (1998)
	Water heating	87	EVA (1998)
	Wet	60	GEA (1995)
	Other	32	Estimate
	TOTAL (LAWH)	520	
	TOTAL – residential	613	IEA/OECD (1998b)
GAS	Ovens	8.8	Kasanen (1999)
	Water heating – LPG	17.5	National data derived
	Water heating - NG	186	National data derived
	Other	75	Estimate
	G-TOTAL (LAWH)	287	IEA/OECD (1998b)

7.2 FUTURE PROJECTIONS / DRIVERS FOR CHANGE

The adoption of the Natural Gas Directive in May 1998 is expected to make a strong contribution to increasing gas demand (European Commission, 1999a), and its provisions are expected to enter into national legislation by the middle of the year 2000 (Stern, 1998). The Gas Directive is expected to help to minimise natural gas prices for consumers, as a result of increased competitiveness among suppliers. As traditional monopolies are opened to competition, the European gas industry will undergo significant restructuring. In Europe, gas is often distributed to end-users along with other services such as electricity, water, district heating, and (more recently) telephone and cable TV services. Local distribution companies normally have monopoly rights and obligations in their supply areas, which reduces competitive pressure from other suppliers, and restricts consumer choice in the provision of services (IEA, 1998).

7.2.1 Household numbers, historical and projected

In 1998, there were over 150 million households in the European Union. This represents an increase of around 40% from the number of households in 1970. Germany accounts for almost one quarter of total EU households, and the four largest countries (Germany, the UK, France and Italy) together constitute 70%. According to official national household projections (supplemented by Euromonitor projections where official data are not available), the total number will approach around 170 million by the year 2010. Euromonitor (1996) projected the fastest rates of growth in household numbers for Ireland, Portugal and Spain.

As shown in Chapter 2 the number of households is an important driver for continued increase in domestic energy consumption, and consequently carbon emissions.

7.3 NATURAL GAS INFRASTRUCTURE AND SUPPLY

The number and proportion of households, which have access to natural gas, varies strikingly across the EU. Countries, in which less than one third of households are connected, can be divided into two groups according to national plans for expansion of the network. That is, those with no immediate plans for further expansion, and those countries where the expansion of the gas network is a prominent element of national energy policy.

7.3.1 Minimal networks

Finland and Sweden have minimal gas networks, with less than 2% of households being supplied with natural gas (Figure 7.1). In both of these countries, natural gas is playing a more prominent role in power generation, district heating and CHP, however further development of the low pressure distribution network depends on Finland's linkage to the continental gas network. Studies are underway to determine the feasibility of this, but there are no plans for expansion in the near future. In Denmark, only a small proportion of households (12%) are connected, however another 27% of households make use of natural gas indirectly through district heating and CHP (Dansk Naturgas, 1999).

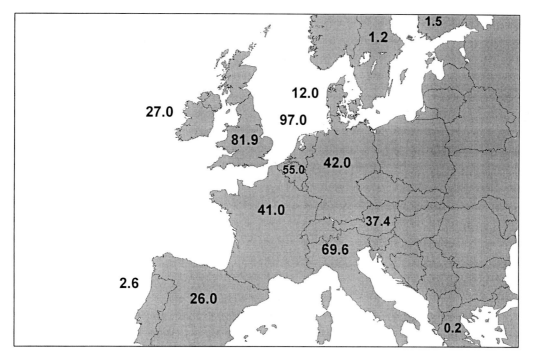

Figure 7.1: Households with natural gas, EU, 1997-9 (%)

7.3.2 New network development

Portugal, Greece and Northern Ireland all have major development projects underway for the construction of a natural gas network:

- the Portuguese natural gas network was planned for completion in 1997. However, technical and financial hurdles are such, that domestic sector penetration is proceeding slowly;
- construction of the low pressure distribution network in Greece is still in the very early stages, and only around 8,000 households in the Athens area had access to natural gas in 1999. A tender for the development of the gas network in the three most highly populated regions of Greece (inhabited by over 50% of the country's population) is underway. Natural gas is considered unlikely to have a dramatic impact on the domestic sector, at least in the near future. The bulk of domestic sector fuel-switching will involve the conversion of oil-fired collective heating systems for apartment buildings. In other respects, the opportunities for fuel-switching in Greek households are limited, (about 21% have solar water heating) and the costs of conversion from other fuels may be prohibitive for individual households;
- domestic consumers in Northern Ireland (part of UK) started to receive natural gas in 1997, after completion of the Scotland to Northern Ireland Pipeline in 1996 (see Appendix N for further details).

7.3.3 Strong continuing development

In Spain and Ireland, the gas network is expanding at a considerable rate, and continuation of this trend constitutes a prominent element of national energy policy. In Spain, for example, the number of domestic consumers grew from 1.9 million in 1990 (17% of households) to 3.16 million in 1997 (27%). The Irish natural gas company Bord Gáis Éireann planned to extend the natural gas supply by at least 18,000 households in 1998, representing a further 6% on the existing customer base of 322,000.

Table 7.2 lists the most recent available estimates for the number of domestic consumers (and the proportion of connected households) in each country. The largest national group of domestic consumers is found in the UK. Germany provides the second largest national consumer group.

Table 7.2: Household with access to the natural gas and annual connections, EU, 1997-9

Country	Households with natural gas (1000s)	% All households	Annual connections*	Source
AU	1,207	37.4	54,500	Eurogas, 1998; Dörfler and Reiss, 1995
BE	2,303	55.0	38,700	Eurogas, 1998; FIGAS, 1997
DK	289	12.0	19,800[1]	Dansk Naturgas, 1999
FI	35	1.5	100	Maakaasuyhdistys, 1998
FR	9,590	41.0	134,400[2]	Eurogas, 1998; GdF, 1999
GE	14,720	42.0	762,500[3]	Ruhrgas, 1999
GR	8	0.2	-[4]	Kouloumoundras, 1999
IR	322	27.0	18,000	BGE, 1999
IT	14,100	69.6	111,000[5]	SNAM, 1999
LU	-			
NL	6,491	97.0	88,000[6]	EnergieNed, 1998;
PO	74	2.6	41,200 projected	ISR, 1999
SP	3,271	26.0	180,280	Sedigas, 1998a
SW	52	1.2	-[7]	Eurogas, 1998
UK	19,897	81.9	255,000	Eurogas, 1998; BG, 1998
EU-15	72,539	48		

Notes:

*often averaged over several years

[1] Rough estimate based on expansion of the distribution network since 1985, and an estimated 297,000 households connected (289,000 households connected plus 8,000 waiting for connection at the end of 1998) at the end of 1999 (Dansk Naturgas, 1999).

[2] Estimate based on GdF (1999) figure of 160,000 new natural gas customers in 1998; Have assumed that the household sector in France is represented in the new connections in the same proportion (84%) it contributes to the overall number of GdF customers.

[3] Refers to annual increase in number of households using natural gas for space heating; in Germany, virtually all households connected to the network use natural gas for space heating (IER, 1998).

[4] No published data available, however it is planned to extend the network into areas serving 50% of the population by 2006; the number of households connected will be much lower than this, especially considering that over 50% of households live in apartment blocks and are unlikely to benefit from gas for water and cooking (domestic sector unlikely to benefit from natural gas immediately).

[5] SNAM data for the expansion of the gas distribution network suggests that the average number of household connections per year between 1992 and 1998 was 195,000 (SNAM, 1999). This is almost twice as large as ENI's figure. SNAM is unlikely to be referring to all customers in the domestic, commercial and residential sector because dividing these figures by household numbers gives around 70%, the expected level of penetration.

[6] No further network development expected in the Netherlands, other than to keep pace with new construction (Ecofys, 1998).

[7] No data, however the domestic market is unlikely to develop further in the near future (Svenska Gasföreningen, 1999).

In 1998, 72 million households (48% of all EU households) were connected to the natural gas network; the proportion is growing at about 1% p.a. Therefore, by 2000, half of all homes in the European Union have the use of natural gas. The most rapid increase in new connections is occurring in (in order) Germany, Austria, Spain, UK, Belgium, the Netherlands, Italy and Denmark.

In 1997, total inland residential gas sales by European Union member states amounted to almost 1,200 TWh, which was 32% of gas sales for all sectors. The largest domestic consumer was the UK, accounting for almost one third of this, with the other significant domestic consumers being Germany, Italy, France and the Netherlands. At the individual household level, Denmark and Austria have the highest levels of natural gas use, followed by Germany, the Netherlands, the UK and Belgium (Table 7.3). Finnish households have relatively low natural gas use: more households use natural gas for cooking (1.4%) than for space or water heating (0.4%). Swedish households may also be more likely to use natural gas for cooking than for heating purposes, as natural gas in Sweden is much more expensive than electricity. Natural gas consumption by individual households in Spain and Italy may be lower than in northern European member states due to the milder climates, however this does not explain the large difference suggested by the data (Eurogas, 1998).

Table 7.3: Total domestic and average household consumption of natural gas, EU, 1998

Country	Total (TWh)	kWh per connected household	Alternative estimates
Austria	28.9	23,900	15,900[1] [1996] (EVA, 1998a)
Belgium	41.3	17,900	19,700 [1997] (FIGAS, 1997)
Denmark	7.4	25,300	25,700 [1998] (Dansk Naturgas, 1999)
Finland	0.25	7,400	7,100 [1996] (Maakaasuyhdistys, 1998)
France	147.8	15,400	11,000 [1996] (IEA/OECD, 1998b)
Germany	294.6	20,000	-
Greece	-	-	-
Ireland	3.7	13,200	-
Italy	187.4	13,300	-
Luxembourg	-	-	-
Netherlands	120.9	18,900	18,500 [1996] (IEA/OECD, 1998b)
Portugal	-	-	7,387 [1998] (ISR, 1998)
Spain	16.6	5,300	-
Sweden	0.6	12,300	17,892 [1996] (IEA/OECD, 1998b)
UK	345.6	17,400	17,400 [1997] (DUKES, 1998)
EU-15	1,198	16,600	

Note: these figures, derived from Eurostat national sales and domestic customer numbers for 1998, can differ significantly from estimates obtained from other sources.

[1]Based on number of households with access to natural gas in 1996, derived from smoothed household connections 1993-1998

Source: Eurogas (1999)

7.4   ELECTRICITY GENERATION AND SUPPLY

The main changes in the EU electricity generation profile since 1970 consist of a large increase in nuclear generation, a slight decrease in the consumption of oil and a corresponding increase in the use of natural gas. Nuclear power's rate of expansion in meeting electricity demand is slowing down. In the future, the share of gas in power generation is expected to grow throughout Europe, as has been happening through the 1990s. This is expected to be the major change in fuel mix in the future, followed by a decrease in solid fuel consumption (European Environment Agency, 1995).

7.4.1   Carbon factors of electricity

The carbon content of electricity varies from one member state to another, as shown earlier in Table 5.4. Most of the projected growth in the natural gas market is expected to come from the power generation sector. The increased use of natural gas is favoured by political aims such as energy security and environmental issues (European Commission, 1999a). Thus in the longer term any substantial reduction in electricity demand will be at the expense of new gas power stations not being built.

In addition, with the liberalisation of the electricity market as a result of the Electricity Directive the EU market should become one market, which means that considering the carbon content of each individual member state becomes less relevant. Any electricity savings though reduced demand in one state could result in the saved electricity being 'exported' to a neighbouring state (as discussed in Chapter 5).

Thus, in this chapter when estimating potential carbon reductions a conversion factor of 0.11 kgC/kWh will be used – the current average of EU production and the figure for a very efficient new gas power generation plant.

7.4.2   Domestic electricity consumption

Electricity consumption by the domestic sector varies across the EU. Household electricity consumption is highest in northern countries, where gas usage is low: Sweden and Finland (Table 7.4). Beyond that simple statement, levels of efficiency, warm winters (and minimal space heating) and the choice of alternative fuels affect the picture. For the other 13 member states, electricity consumption varies within the narrow range of 2,700-5,600 kWh pa per household. This is discussed further under the separate end-uses.

Table 7.4: Total domestic and average household consumption of electricity, EU, 1996

Country	TWh	kWh per household	Alternative estimates (source)
Austria	13.3	4,200	4,500 [1996] (EVA, 1998a)
Belgium	23.3	5,600	3,900 [1997] (BFE, 1998)
Denmark	10.9	4,600	3,300 (Bach, 1999) [1998]; 4,400 (DEA ,1998) [1997]
Finland	17.2	7,600	-
France	120.5	5,100	-
Germany	134.2	3,600	3,500 [1995] (VDEW, 1996)
Greece	12.2	3,700	3,839 [1996] (NSSG, 1999)
Ireland	5.7	5,000	4,800 [1996] (ESB, 1999); 4,200 [1995] (IEC, 1996)
Italy	58.0	2,700	-
Luxembourg	0.7	4,800	-
Netherlands	20.0	3,100	-
Portugal	8.5	2,900	-
Spain	37.6	3,000	-
Sweden	43.3	10,400	-
UK	107.6	4,500	5,300 [1997] (DUKES, 1998)
EU-15	612.9	4,100	-

Source: IEA/OECD, 1998b; European Commission, 1999a

7.4.3   Potential for reduction

Using this information, and the detailed analysis carried out for the three studied countries, it is possible to provide a rough estimate of the potential savings under the ETP and Kyoto+ scenario if the analysis were repeated for the whole of the EU.

The average EU household uses 4,100 kWh of electricity; approximately 80% of this is used for LAWH, the remainder is for space heating. Of this 3,280 kWh, the economic and technical potential reduction, based on the three partner countries, is 28% by 2010. That is, almost 1,000 kWh of electricity could potentially be saved per household in Europe, by 2010: a total of 140 TWh. The policies proposed in the Kyoto+ scenario would realise around 85% of this potential, or about 120 TWh, the equivalent cf 13MtC (assuming the current average EU conversion factor is the savings conversion factor). This is similar to the value if estimates of potential savings are done by end-use. This end-use analysis of potential savings now follows and is summarised in the conclusions to this chapter.

7.5   WATER HEATING

The largest end-use of gas covered by this study is for heating water (space heating is not considered). Furthermore, improvements in the energy efficiency of housing and space heating systems, and increasing demands for domestic comfort, mean that water heating is becoming a more significant element of the household fuel bill. In most cold countries, domestic space heating consumes three times as much energy as domestic water heating. However, in Portugal and countries where space heating is not common, water heating can consume more than three times as much energy as space heating.

7.5.1   Ownership

The majority of households in the EU have centralised water heating systems, in which hot water from the household is supplied by one central (often storage) water heater. Such systems are also known as 'multi-point' systems, as opposed to 'single-point', in which each point of use is supplied with a separate, independent (usually instantaneous) water heater. The main exception to this is Germany, in which decentralised instantaneous systems are more common than centralised storage systems (EVA, 1998).

Despite general improvements in living standards, in some countries the proportion of households without any hot water system remains significant: Greece (18%); Ireland (5%) (Eurostat, 1998; EVA, 1998). Those without hot water are more likely to be low-income households (Eurostat, 1998).

Water heating ownership data were collected for two main parameters: fuel type, and whether or not the systems for heating space and water were integrated. Other important parameters, for which it was not possible to collect detailed data, include the size of the water tank and the degree of insulation. Average water heater size varies widely across the EU. For example, 65% of French storage water heaters are of a capacity greater than 150 litres, compared to Germany, where 73% of the stock are 15 litres or below (EVA, 1998). In the Netherlands, there is a trend towards larger (predominantly storage) water heaters, due to rising standards of household comfort (EnergieNed, 1998).

Fuel type

The four main fuels for hot water in EU households are gas, oil, electricity and district heating. In the UK, Italy and the Netherlands, the most important fuel is natural gas (Table 7.5). The average household in each of these countries, however, is in a quite different situation: for example, most UK households are supplied with hot water from a natural gas-fired boiler, that also supplies the central heating, while the majority of Dutch households have separate (gas-fired) appliances. Only around 50% of the German households with access to the natural gas network, use natural gas for water heating: they tend to have small instantaneous gas-fired heaters, and the remainder are most likely to use electricity. LPG is most widely used in Portugal for instantaneous water heating (almost two-thirds of households); electric water heating predominates in France, Germany and Sweden; oil and solid fuels in Ireland, and district heating has the largest share of the Danish market. In Germany and Sweden respectively, coal-fired and wood-fired storage boilers are commonly owned (GasTec, 1996).

Table 7.5 : Main water heating fuel, EU (% of households)

Country	Electricity	Gas (natural gas and LPG)	Year	Source
AU	44 *	-	1997	EVA, 1998
BE	33 *	-	1997	EVA, 1998
DK	13 *	12	1997/8	EVA, 1998; Dansk Naturgas, 1999
FI	28	0.4	1995	Statistics Finland, 1998
FR	45	37	1997	CEREN, 1998
GE	45	20	1995	GasTec, 1996
GR	5 *	-	1997	EVA, 1998
IR	17	17	1995	IEC, 1996
IT	33 *	54	1995	GasTec, 1996
LU	45 *	-	1997	EVA, 1998
NL	17 *	89	1997	EVA, 1998; EnergieNed, 1998
PO	19 *	64 #	1997	EVA, 1998; CCE/INE (ISR, 1998)
SP	17 *	-	1997	EVA, 1998
SW	~ 50	~ 5	1995	GasTec, 1996
UK	19	71	1991	DETR, 1999c

Note: numbers can exceed 100% where households have two main systems
* *Storage water heaters only*
# *LPG-fired water heating only*

Ownership of electric storage water heaters in particular, and electric water heating in general, is declining across the EU, and this decline is projected to continue (EVA, 1998). The trend towards natural gas is particularly marked in Italy and the UK, in both of which the penetration of combination boilers is growing, and it is accompanied throughout the EU by decreasing popularity of independent instantaneous water heaters, both electric and gas (BSRIA, 1995; EVA, 1998).

Combined versus non-combined space and water heating systems

As a general rule, households dependent upon electricity have separate systems for space and water heating (CEREN, 1998). Whereas those using gas are increasingly likely to have one combined system. With these, the same boiler is used for both space and water heating. These can either be instantaneous or with stored hot water in a cylinder, and both instantaneous and stored can utilise a condensing boiler.

There are thus four separate trends in EU water heating - towards more: gas-fired systems; combined gas systems; instantaneous systems; and condensing boilers.

Where there is a combined system, the savings from improved boiler efficiency benefit both end uses, not just water heating, as discussed here.

While solar technologies still have minimal market share for water heating in the EU, where they do exist they are the sole form of heating in the summer months and provide background heat at other times. It is most widespread in Greece, where 95% of the total installed solar power collection area is dedicated to water heating. Approximately 21% of Greek households (850,000) use solar water heating systems – the number may be higher - and they continue to increase in popularity due to special tax exemptions. The high price of electricity in Greece means installation costs can be recuperated within a period of 4-5 years (Fyrogenis 1999). Around 5% of new dwellings in Denmark are constructed with the capacity to heat water by solar power. The main obstacles to increasing the share of solar water heating are architectural preferences for 'the traditional' and the excessively long payback times for solar technology (DEA, 1999). The payback is affected by the size and complexity of the system (Greek ones are highly standardised, simple and low cost), the need to protect from frost and reduced sunshine hours in winter, as well as the cost of the replacement fuel.

7.5.2   Energy consumption

Electric storage water heaters consumed around 87 TWh in 1997. This is assumed to fall to 78 TWh by the year 2020, due to an ongoing decline in the ownership of electric storage water heaters (EVA, 1998), which are gradually being replaced by natural gas-fired water heating. There are few data available for the overall consumption of natural gas by EU water heating. It appears that energy consumption for domestic hot water is still on the increase across the EU, but that the rate of growth is faster for natural gas than for electricity.

In Italy, electricity consumption for domestic water heating has increased from 4 TWh in 1970 to almost 10 TWh in 1996, and natural gas consumption rose over the same period from 4 TWh to 23 TWh (ENEA, 1999). Natural gas consumption for water heating is increasing in the Netherlands (EnergieNed, 1998) and there have been significant increases in electricity and LPG consumption for water heating in Portugal (ISR, 1999). Prognos (1995) projected national energy consumption for water heating in Germany to rise until the year 2000, after which it is expected to start to decline. National energy consumption in France appears to be fairly constant (CEREN, 1998). In Denmark, individual household consumption for domestic hot water has been falling, largely because of a drop in hot water consumption. This is due to a new water consumption tax and an additional cost element in the water rates, which has made the water for a shower more expensive than the energy used to heat it (DEA, pers. comm., 1999).

Table 7.6 : Consumption of electricity and natural gas for domestic hot water, EU (TWh)

Country	Electricity	Natural gas	All fuels[1]	Year	Source
AU	1.9	2.4	8.4	1996	EVA,1998a
BE	2.3	-	-	1997	BFE, 1998
DK	-	-	8.3	1994	DEA, 1995; DEF, 1999
FI	3.1	-	-	1996	Finergy/Sener, 1998
FI	2.1	0.04	7.6	1995	Statistics Finland, 1998
FR	5.4	6.3	16.9	1997	CEREN, 1998
GE	16.3[2]	25.6[2]	70.4[2]	1995	Prognos, 1995
GR	2.2	-	-	1997	PPC, 1999
IR	0.49	0.32	2.92	1995	IEC, 1996
IT	9.54	22.62	37.12	1996	ENEA, 1999
LU	-				
NL	3.7 (1995)	20.9 (1996)	-	1995/6	BEK, 1996; BAK, 1997
PO	0.55	0.32	3.95	1997	ISR, 1999
SP	-				
SW	-				
UK	13.9	93.6	122.4	1996	DTI, 1997
EU-15	87	186			

[1] All domestic fuels including coal, oil and wood
[2] Projected consumption

The 72 million households in Europe connected to the gas network use an annual average of 2560 kWh of gas for water heating, to give a European total of 186 TWh, or 15% of total domestic gas use. A further 87 TWh of electricity are used for water heating (Table 7.6, EVA 1998), which is 14% of total domestic electricity.

7.5.3   Potential reduction

A rough estimate of the potential reductions in energy consumption for the whole of the EU, if the Kyoto+ scenario were implemented, can be obtained by using the above information. The scenario will reduce carbon emissions be improving the efficiency of gas and electric water heaters and switch some of the electric water heating to gas.

In the three countries a saving of 8% can be made through increased gas boiler efficiency by 2010 if replacement and new boilers are at the level described in the Kyoto+ scenario. Thus around 15 TWh of gas could be saved for water heating alone across the EU if the Kyoto+ Scenario were implemented. If the losses are included - and also space heating when combined with the water heating in one system - the potential savings would be much larger.

The DESWH study (EVA 1998) showed that the potential for reducing electricity was 2 TWh by 2010, as a result of new appliances having increased insulation.

The potential for reducing carbon by fuel switching is dependent on the extent of the gas network. For this analysis, it is assumed that half of the electric water heating in 2010 will be replaced by natural gas. In this case 41 TWh of electricity will be displaced and replaced by (slightly higher) gas consumption.

An EU-wide water heating study is currently under way that will throw further light onto the energy consumption by water heating, the associated carbon emissions and the potential to improve the efficiency of water heating systems.

7.6   APPLIANCES AND LIGHTING

Electricity consumption by domestic appliances and lighting, discussed in this section, is a major source of carbon emitted by EU households.

7.6.1   Ownership

The level of ownership of different appliances varies between different member states and is influenced by economic factors, cultural factors and climate. Levels of ownership of several large appliances are given in Table 7.7.

Some appliances, such as cold appliances (penetration levels are around 98-99% in all EU countries) and washing machines, can be considered to be integral to European standards of living and are owned by the vast majority of households. Colour television sets are also very widely owned in the EU, being at near saturation level in many member states (ONS, 1998) with multiple ownership common.

A dishwasher can be considered to be a luxury appliance. Ownership is largely dependent on economic factors and the size of the household, being relatively high in Finland (40%) and Sweden (49%), countries known for high standards of living and high levels of appliance ownership. Tumble dryers can also be considered to be luxury appliances, however ownership levels are strongly influenced by climate and culture. Italian households are least likely to own tumble dryers; Portugal and Spain also having relatively low ownership levels. While rain-soaked countries such as the UK, Denmark and the Netherlands have ownership levels of one third or more.

In general, southern member states tend to have lower levels of consumer durable ownership. This may be only partly due to differences in living standards, since cultural factors are also important. For example, Greece and the UK are comparable in terms of their low dishwasher ownership (17% and 20% respectively), however the UK is generally considered to be a more prosperous member state than Greece, with relatively higher levels of ownership of consumer durables.

Table 7.7 : Ownership of selected electrical appliances by country

Country	Ownership (% households)							
	Freezer	Fridge-freezer	Washing machine	Tumble -dryer	Dish-washer	Colour TV	VCR	PC
AU	67	-	91	11	43	-	-	-
BE	61	36	88	52	34	95	63[1]	32
DK	61	43	71	30	34	120	-	45
FI	80	-	83[2]	9[2]	41[2]	95	61[2]	28[2]
FR	52	-	91	25	38	93	68	-
GE	68	-	94	26	42	97	67	-
GR	-	-	-	-	17[1]	87	39[1]	-
IR	23	49	86	26	19	98	65	16
IT	30	-	94	1	23	97	52	12
LU	-	-	-	-	54[1]	97	64[1]	-
NL	56	47	98	52	25	98	80	57
PO	51	-	79	7	16	83	46	14
SP	20	-	96	8	19	97	66	-
SW	73	-	77	27	49	100	60[1]	-
UK	42	60	91	51	20	96	89	27

Note: *All reference dates for 1996/97, as in general and country-specific sources, except ownership of colour TV's and data marked with [1] (1994) and [2] (1995).*

Sources: *Appliance 1997; BFE 1999 (Belgium); CSO 1999 (Ireland); DECADE 1997 (UK); DEF 1999 (Denmark); EnergieNed 1998 (Netherlands); Finergy/Sener 1998 (Finland); Statistics Finland (1998); IEC 1996 (Ireland); ISR 1999 (Portugal); ISTAT 1998 (Italy).*

Certain countries have unique patterns of appliance ownership because of the cultural importance of a specific appliance, which may be rare in other countries. For example, the appliance profile of Finnish households is distinguished not only by high levels of appliance ownership compared to other countries, but by ownership of a sauna stove. In recent years, levels of sauna ownership have soared, such that 90% of dwellings (including some flats) were estimated to own a sauna in 1998, compared to just under 40% in 1990. It is estimated that around 60% of sauna stoves are electric, giving over one million electric sauna stoves in Finland as a whole (TTS, pers. comm., 1999).

Appliance ownership continues to increase in all member states, as the equipment becomes more accessible in economic terms. It is likely that the projected economic growth in Spain, Portugal and Greece will lead to increases in appliance ownership levels in these countries, although it is difficult to estimate at what level of ownership saturates for appliances such as fridge-freezers, tumble dryers, dishwashers and home computers.

7.6.2   Energy consumption

The highest levels of individual household electricity consumption for lights and appliances (excluding cooking) are found in Finland and Sweden, followed by Denmark (Figure 7.2). The European average is 2,500 kWh, which represents 60% of all residential electricity use (4,100 kWh per household – Table 7.4).

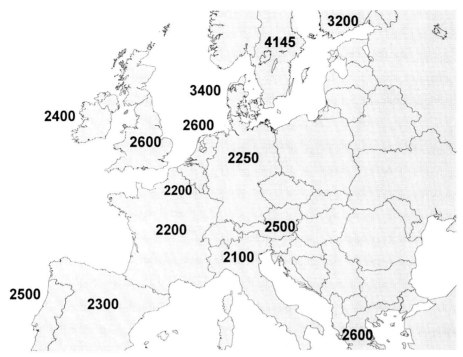

Figure 7.2 : Average annual household electricity consumption for domestic lights and appliances, excluding cooking, EU (kWh)

On a per household basis, there appear to be variations in the importance of different appliances in total appliance electricity consumption. For example, cold appliances are the most energy-consuming sector in French households, the UK and Greece, while wet appliances comprise the largest part of appliance electricity demand in Germany, Denmark and the Netherlands. Consideration also needs to be made for appliances that are common in one or more countries and rare in others, such as sauna stoves in Finland, and kettles in the UK.

Despite technological improvements in appliance efficiency, electricity consumption by domestic appliances and lighting continues to increase. In Italy, electricity consumption by appliances has increased around threefold since 1970 (ENEA, 1999). Figure 7.3 (a and b) shows available time series data for certain countries. Of these, the rise in consumption is most marked in Germany, the UK and Italy. Electricity consumption by appliances in Denmark has remained fairly stable despite the continual increase in appliance ownership. This, and a similar pattern in Finland, is due to technological improvements in appliance efficiency and (possibly) to changes in consumer behaviour (Bach, 1999). Overall consumption by Danish lights and appliances is expected to begin to decline around the year 2000 (DEA, 1995). Appliance consumption in Germany is projected to go into decline after 2005 (Prognos, 1995). In France, recent growth in appliance ownership has placed a strain on electricity distribution networks, particularly at peak demand (EdF, 1999).

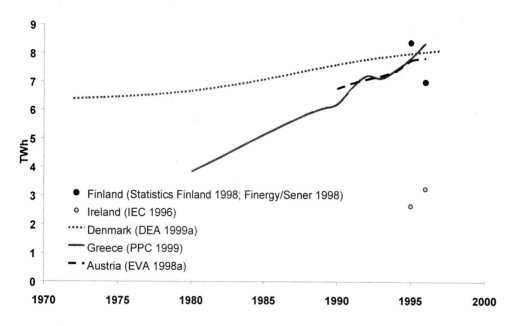

Figure 7.3a: Trends in electricity consumption for domestic electrical appliances and lighting (excluding cooking): Austria, Denmark, Finland, Greece, Ireland

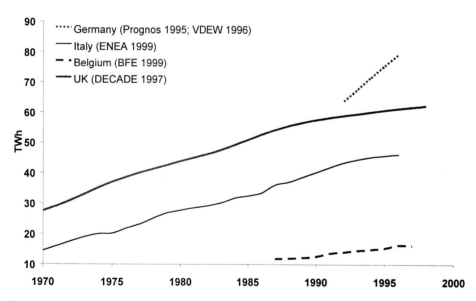

Figure 7.3b: Trends in electricity consumption for domestic electrical appliances and lighting (excluding cooking): Belgium, Germany, Italy, UK

Within the EU, Denmark appears to be the only country to have effectively stabilised domestic energy consumption. In Denmark, from 1990-92 the electricity consumption in households without electric heating increased by 2.8%. There was no increase from 1992-95, it seems there has been a saturation of consumption, as a result of policies on energy efficiency and fuel switching.

The reasons given for this decrease include:
- number of energy efficient light bulbs has increased;
- burning hours of lighting have decreased;
- more efficient cold appliances in the stock;
- more microwave ovens leading to lower cooking energy consumption;
- dramatic decrease in the number of water beds (Bach, 1999).

Three of these five explanations are to do with ownership of more efficient equipment, one to do with usage, and one to do with decreasing ownership of an appliance.

7.6.3   Potential reduction

A detailed look at the evidence on energy savings for each of the partner countries was undertaken in Chapter 3 (see also Appendix F). The analysis was based on the knowledge of various EU-wide studies that have taken place. These are now used to inform the analysis to estimate the likely effects on EU carbon emissions of implementing the Kyoto+ Scenario.

Cold appliances

Cold appliances across the EU currently consume around 109 TWh (Waide 1999), and should decline as a result of the 1999 minimum efficiency standards and national governments providing rebates for the more efficient appliances. If the decline in consumption is the same as for the three countries studied in detail in this report, consumption would decline to 98TWh by 2010. If new appliances reached the efficiency level described in the Kyoto+ scenario then electricity consumption would fall by a further 20TWh.

Lighting

Current EU consumption by lighting is around 89TWh and is expected to increase to 97TWh by 2010 (derived from DELight 1998). As with the current study, DELight (1998) described a policy scenario where CFLs replace incandescent bulbs where they are cost-effective to the consumer. If the Kyoto+ scenario is implemented then electricity consumption by lighting would be reduced by 27TWh by 2010.

Wet appliances

An EU-wide study in 1995 estimated that consumption by washing machines, dishwashers and tumble dryers would increase from 59 TWh in 1994 to more than 68 TWh in 2016. These values have been interpolated, then using the same level of energy reduction as for the three countries studied; EU energy consumption reduces by 11 TWh in 2010, if the Kyoto+ Scenario were implemented.

Miscellaneous

An EU-wide 1997 study on miscellaneous standby estimated consumption to rise from 20 TWh to 50TWh by 2010 (Molinder, 1997). The likely increase is substantial and a large part is attributed to the expected uptake of receiver-decoders. A high efficiency scenario examined in the study estimated that consumption could be reduced by 30 TWh in 2010.

7.7   COOKING

Definitional issues bedevil debates about the use of energy for cooking. There are free-standing cookers (all one fuel), separate, built-in ovens and hobs (same or different fuels) and numerous smaller appliances, such as microwaves and kettles that might or might not be included in the statistics. The recent EU ovens study (Kasanen, 1999) has clarified some of the issues, but the following figures may still be somewhat inconsistent and should be taken as indicative.

7.7.1   Ownership

Approximately 70% of EU households use electricity as the primary fuel source for cooking, and 20% use natural (piped) or LPG (bottled) gas (Table 7.8). The remaining 10% use other fuels. The ownership of natural gas cooking facilities clearly depends on the development of the gas distribution network for domestic consumers in each country, but of those with natural gas (48% in 1998), less than 20% use it for cooking, indicating considerable carbon savings potential.

Consumer trends in cooking appliance purchasing are leading to a gradual decline in the ownership of gas ovens, and a corresponding increase in electric oven ownership throughout the EU. This shift has taken place fairly rapidly in Austria and the Netherlands, and more slowly in the UK, France, Germany, Italy and Denmark. Reasons for the switch may include consumer perceptions of electric ovens as having better performance, more features and more effective self-cleaning cycles than gas ovens. In Sweden and

Finland, electric ovens are the majority appliance due to the limited development of the domestic gas infrastructure, and the situation in both these countries is unlikely to change in the near future.

Table 7.8 : Principal cooking facilities, or main oven, by fuel, EU (% of households owning)

Country	Electricity	(NG & LPG)	Year	Source
AU	77	20	1993	Wolf and Kronsteiner, 1995
BE	53	-	1997	CEG, 1998
DK	88	6[1]	1998	DEA, 1998; Dansk Naturgas, 1999
FI	99	1.4	1997	Adato Energia Oy, 1998; Maakaasuyhdistys, 1998
FR	49	50	1995	Kasanen, 1999
GE	81	19	1996	VDEW, 1996
GR	-	-		
IR	51	32[2]	1995	IEC, 1996
IT	60	40	1997	Doxa S.p.A., 1998
LU	-	-		
NL	62	21	1996	BAK ,1997; BEK, 1996
PO	20	78		
SP	12	85	1998	Kasanen, 1999
SW	96	4	1997	Konsumenverket, pers. Comm., 1998
UK	56	41	1996	DECADE, 1997(b); LEEP, 1996
EU-15	70	20		

[1] *1% of households used mains gas for cooking, however a further 5% used town gas produced from natural gas; 6% of households owned a gas oven in 1995, and 13% a gas hob (DEA 1998)*
[2] *All gas, of which natural gas = 10.5%; LPG and manufactured gas = 20.1%; combined gas and electricity = 0.8% (IEC 1996)*

Through a comparison of Table 7.8 and Figure 7.1, it is apparent that LPG for cooking is prevalent in some countries, even where there is an extensive gas network. For instance, in France 41% of households are on the natural gas network, but 50% use either natural gas or LPG for cooking. In Ireland, comparable figures are 27% and 32%. As there are 20% carbon dioxide savings available when natural gas displaces LPG, this is a useful policy option in several countries, if the gas network is present or expanded.

7.7.2 Energy consumption

A total of 125 TWh of delivered energy is used for cooking in Europe: 74TWh of gas and 51TWh of electricity giving an annual household consumption of 830 kWh. Cooking use represents 8% of all residential electricity consumption and 6% of gas. About 18% of all cooking energy is used in ovens (Kasanen, 1999), with most of the remainder going into hobs.

Cooking is one of the most user-dependent end-uses in terms of energy consumption. National data reflect not only household numbers but also cultural preferences in cooking practices. Natural gas is the most important cooking fuel (in terms of final energy consumption measured in GWh) in France, Italy and the UK. The countries with the highest electricity demand by cooking appliances are Germany, the UK and France. In virtually all countries, use of the oven is declining, due to changing eating patterns (such as increasing use of microwaves and consumption of frozen and pre-prepared foods), and reduced levels of occupancy (and hence more meals consumed outside the home). In addition, the ongoing decrease in household size and increase in one-person households, will also mean average usage will decline since these households are less likely to use the oven.

7.7.3 Potential reduction

There are significant carbon savings from:

- more efficient electric ovens;
- more efficient electric hobs;
- and some fuel switching.

Using the information from the three countries, consumption by electric cooking is expected to decline to 45TWh across the EU by 2010. Using the same scaling again, the potential to reduce consumption through more efficient appliances under the Kyoto+ Scenario is around 7 TWh. Most of this is through more efficient electric hobs, though around 2TWh are from more efficient ovens (Kasanen, 1999).

The wider use of natural gas, will result in considerable carbon savings across Europe given present electric appliance efficiency. To demonstrate the potential order of magnitude of carbon reductions, it has been assumed that one third of the electricity is displaced by gas cooking by 2010. In this case 15 TWh of electricity will be displaced by gas.

7.8 CONCLUSIONS

Electricity consumption across the EU is still rising, primarily due to an increase in household numbers and increasing ownership of appliances and lighting.

As shown in the last chapter for the UK, NL and PO there are substantial energy savings and carbon reductions to be made through the introduction of more efficient LAWH. Replicating the analysis of the previous chapter, the data presented in this chapter would result in total gas and electricity consumption of 756 TWh being reduced by 141 TWh (19%) (Table 7.9).

Table 7.9 Potential EU energy savings and carbon reductions through improved efficiency

	RC, 1998	RC, 2010	RC-Kyoto+, 2010	RC-Kyoto+, 2010
ELECTRIC	Energy (TWh)	Energy (TWh)	Energy savings (TWh)	Carbon reductions (MtC)
CE (less misc standby)	72	75	22.5	2.47
CE - Misc standby	20	50	30	3.30
Cold	109	98	19	2.09
Cooking	51	45	7	0.77
Lighting	89	97	27	2.96
Water heating	87	82	2	0.24
Wet	60	65	11	1.21
Other	32	32	0	0.00
TOTAL (LAWH)	**520**	**545**	**123**	**13.47**
TOTAL – residential	613			
GAS	(TWh)	(TWh)	(TWh)	(MtC)
Ovens	8.8	7.5	0.5	0.03
LPG WH	17.5	17.5	1	0.08
NG WH	186	186	16	0.82
G-TOTAL (LAWH)	**287**	**211**	**18**	**0.92**

This sketchy, preliminary analysis has demonstrated that the polices in the Kyoto+ scenario, if applied to the whole of Europe, would save in excess of 14MtC by 2010 through improved efficiency. These would make a significant contribution to the expected EU carbon gap of 118MtC (derived from www.eea.dk), across all sectors. The Kyoto+ Scenario would deliver further substantial savings (unquantified here) where the same efficient boilers are providing space heating as well as hot water.

Major potential carbon reductions arise from the more efficient use of electric lights, refrigeration and consumer electronic appliances. The main emphasis continues to be on the more efficient use of electricity, partly because this is the more polluting fuel in most the EU, but also because product-level policy is the easiest to implement. The powerful approach of market transformation strategies, if supported by strong EU commitments, can improve the efficient of products with certainty and speed. Guaranteed savings are available but depend on the Commission, Council and Parliament to be more active.

Efficiency improvements to gas boilers do reduce gas consumption significantly though it does not provide large reductions in carbon by 2010, when compared to the potential reduction by electric appliances and lighting. This is due to several factors. By 2010, the natural rate of turnover means that much less than half of all, older and less efficient, boilers will have been replaced. Also, additional carbon reductions (above the 1MtC listed above) will arise as a result of this increased efficiency since standing and distribution losses have not been included in this analysis – only the energy required to heat the water. In addition, if the boiler is part of a combined space and water heating system, as is becoming more prevalent in Europe, much larger savings from space heating will accrue at the same time. Hence the reduction of 1MtC is a large underestimate of the potential carbon reduction if boilers become more efficient across Europe.

Piped domestic gas is becoming the norm, with perhaps 70% of all EU households connected by 2020. Therefore, fuel switching from electric to gas at the household level is relevant on the national level and increasingly so for EU policy. Fuel switching, in order to reduce carbon emissions, should be directed primarily towards water heating. The opportunities from saving from cooking and tumble dryers will decrease significantly when the projected improvements in efficiency of their electric counterparts under Kyoto+ are reached (see Chapter 3). The potential reduction in carbon is significant, around 3MtC (Table 7.10).

Table 7.10: Potential effects of fuel-switching across EU

	RC, 1998	RC, 2010	Kyoto+, 2010	Kyoto+, 2010	Kyoto+, 2010
	Energy (TWh)	Energy (TWh)	Reduced Electicity (TWh)	Increased Gas (TWh)	Net carbon Reducion (MtC)
Cooking	51	45	15	17.3	0.75
Tumble dryers	9	10	3	3.5	0.15
Water heating	87	82	41	47.2	2.06
FS-TOTAL	147	137	59	68	3

However, few policies have been identified that would trigger or encourage this switch to happen, though national considerations and policy priorities will drive most of the changes. The most obvious national policy approach would be through national building codes to ensure that all new build houses are as carbon-efficient as possible from the beginning. The development of the carbon market could provide consumers and industry with both the information and the incentive to encourage fuel-switching.

The estimated potential carbon reductions from fuel-switching is from consumers choosing gas rather than electric. However, there will be some reduction in carbon emissions if consumers switch from bottled LPG to piped natural gas (over 20% reduction in carbon emissions per delivered kWh). LPG water heating and cooking is common in some countries where there is no piped network. However, not all this potential will be realised since there is some evidence (Portugal DSM, Appendix P) that switching from LPG to NG increases consumption, especially for water heating where there is always access to gas; with bottled LPG there is a limit due to running out of LPG supplies.

Where district heating exists, there is the potential to reduce carbon emissions using heat-fed appliances, as shown in Chapter 3. There is an extensive domestic network in Denmark that could use this technology. Attaching the heat-fed appliances to a central water heating system could also reduce emissions though the cost-effectiveness is less certain at present. Increased scale of production could reduce costs sufficiently, to be viable when connected to a household's central water heating system.

In performing this broad-scope analysis, it is apparent that there is still no robust reference case for Europe. However, major carbon reductions, especially from electrical efficiency are possible as shown in the Kyoto+ Scenario. This also confirms the need for minimum standards (and a framework directive).

Policies investigated in detail (Kyoto+ Scenario) for UK, NL, PO in the previous chapter could be replicated throughout EU and would yield carbon reductions of the order of 17TWh.

CHAPTER 8: CONCLUSIONS – THE PATH TO LOWER CARBON FUTURES

In this chapter the steps required by various actors in order that the Kyoto+ savings are achieved are described (Section 8.1). Then priorities for further research are identified (Section 8.2), followed by a few concluding remarks (Section 8.3).

8.1   NEXT STEPS

A wide-ranging study, such as this, has implications for many different actors, from the member state to the individual consumer. These are summarised so that, hopefully, every reader can be clear about the next task.

Manufacturers of electrical equipment

The more careful use of electricity is the prime message in this report. Electrical equipment has been getting more energy efficient through autonomous improvements and those motivated by government and industry policy. The need is now to double this rate of improvement, where ownership levels are static. Where the market is still expanding rapidly, for instance consumer electronics, there should be greater reductions in unit energy consumption, to minimise the net effect. There are numerous opportunities for a focus on reduced energy consumption, for instance in the various set-top boxes, but these require the co-ordination of component manufacturers and service providers, at a minimum.

The route to these reductions may well be through industry agreements that are negotiated by the trade associations. It is in everyone's interest if these are promoted by the industry at a challenging level. The most ambitious targets should be in areas where there are major savings available - particularly the cold appliances and lighting - and where there is competition with an alternative fuel, usually gas. In most of Europe, the use of electricity causes greater pollution than gas, so that electrical appliances have to be super-efficient to avoid the call for fuel switching. The development of a carbon economy will shift the focus from energy efficiency to low carbon emissions.

Manufacturers of gas equipment

The liberalisation of the gas industry has reduced gas prices - noticeably in the UK, where the process is well developed. At these lower prices, there are few energy efficiency improvements in gas appliances that are cost effective for the consumer. There may well, therefore, be little government policy to promote technology improvements. There will, however, be an emphasis on the wider use of gas in domestic households to reduce carbon dioxide emissions. The future could be of an expanding market for sales with little pressure to develop new technologies. In these circumstances, the industry has a special obligation to look at the opportunities for greater efficiency and lower carbon dioxide emissions.

A further reason for the gas industry to focus on efficiency is that this will maintain gas' position as a low carbon use, even if electrical appliances increase in efficiency substantially.

Both manufacturers

The reducing size of families and the growth in the number of one-person households means that new innovative types of equipment are needed: compact cold appliances, stronger marketing of combination ovens and microwaves, washing machines that are efficient with 1kg loads. Most of the growth in energy demand is coming from the increasing number of households, despite the fact that they are smaller. Manufacturers can help to offset this trend with the products they develop.

Electricity and gas utilities

The phrase 'integrated resource planning' has gone out of fashion, but the emphasis in this report on carbon represents a clear form of IRP. If energy services are measured in terms of the carbon produced to provide them, there is a single focus to policy. Low carbon electricity (renewables), low carbon delivered energy (gas) and reduced consumption (energy efficiency) will all combine to minimise the carbon emissions per household. The utilities can develop policies and approaches that move towards a carbon based economy in the domestic sector. The example of AUCH (average utility carbon per household) was cited to show how the utility could combine environmental policy, demand and supply decisions in one framework.

To complement the carbon-based approach of the suppliers, there needs to be a growth of awareness amongst householders of their impact on the environment. The inclusion of information on the household bill of the amount of carbon dioxide emitted by that level of consumption would start to educate consumers. It is strongly hoped that the utilities will begin to experiment with more informative bills and establish the most appropriate format. Feedback, through comparing consumption in this period with that of a comparable one last year, has been shown to trigger more careful behaviour and reduce bills by up to 10%. This would be supported by the development of more intelligent meters that provide information on consumption, costs and carbon emissions.

For the gas utilities, there is also the expectation that the gas network will be expanded to more households, as rapidly as possible. This is a clear marketing opportunity, but one that also has strong environmental benefits.

Gas installers and the supply chain

The stock of water heating appliances in the Netherlands is very efficient, whereas in the UK it is not. There are few good explanations for the difference, but one solution is better training in energy efficiency for the British installers. In the past, the emphasis has been on safety issues and this now needs to be complemented by a focus on reduced consumption - for the health of future generations.

The increased awareness of energy efficiency amongst installers would also facilitate the removal of the many old, inefficient boilers in people's homes. When a gas appliance is serviced, advice should be given automatically if there are savings of more than 20% to be made through new equipment.

At a more general level, the skills and expertise of those who visit consumers in the home should be of the highest standard. There are limited opportunities to get alternative advice - and it feels impolite to doubt the integrity of the person standing in front of you. As a result, many householders only obtain one quote for replacement systems. Whilst the example here relates to gas water heating, it is true of double glazing salespeople and, increasingly, to doorstep selling of solar water heaters.

Retail outlets

The majority of domestic appliances are bought in retail showrooms by the consumer. The store has a substantial role in both providing advice about efficiency levels (the meaning and importance of the energy label) and in the choice of appliances that are stocked. A consumer cannot purchase efficient equipment that is not stocked. The promotion of aggregated purchase across Europe (through Energy+/ICECAP) has been instrumental in helping retailers recognise the marketing opportunities of environmental concern. The Energy+ project is supported by a multitude of European organisations. They are gathered in three main groups: Energy+ retailers, institutional buyers and supporters. Together they represent more than 15,000 retail outlets and more than a million dwellings.

The circle of decision-makers - manufacturers, retailers and consumers - all have to be working together for energy efficient products to end up in the home. The greater involvement of retailers is evident and welcome.

Consumer representatives and environmental groups

These groups have a dual role: to encourage many of these commercial actors to perform, as well as in raising awareness in the general population. There are substantial financial benefits for consumers from greater energy efficiency, but the majority of householders do not realise this. Life-cycle costing is not the normal activity of the Saturday morning shopper, so the price of the appliance dominates the purchase decision.

There are individuals, who are motivated by a concern for the environment or lower running costs, but they, on their own, cannot shift the whole market. Using the energy label, requiring a condensing boiler, searching for compact fluorescent bulbs will all nudge the stock in the right direction, but slowly. The greater the proportion of the population that recognises energy efficiency as an important component of appliance performance, the more effective policy is. Customer environmental awareness and the effectiveness of policy go hand-in-hand.

For those who represent the poorest households there is a special obligation. The most effective way to save energy is through minimum standards - only efficient appliances can be produced. However, if, as now, consumption continues to grow and efficiency improvements are minimal, the pressure will grow for the price of electricity and gas to be increased through taxes. Where this would be regressive for low-income households, pressure groups have to demand product-based policies to avoid the need for fiscal measures. Environmentalists are recognizing this as well, but there could be greater pressure to sacrifice today's poor for the good of future generations.

A further role for the poverty lobby is to ensure that energy efficiency policies benefit all sectors in society. The market transformation approach does not automatically benefit low-income households - the objective has to be designed into the strategy and this can be expensive. But if this does not occur, then, relatively, the poor become more disadvantaged. It is only the rich that obtain the efficiency improvements, partly because many of the less affluent depend upon the second-hand market.

Environmental awareness and recognition of the need for sustainability will have wider effects in future. Society will need to choose a better quality of life, rather than a higher standard of living. To choose a cleaner, healthier, less-threatening climate rather than ever increasing material possessions. Moving to a carbon-based economy will be the first stage in that process.

European Commission
The major legislative framework depends on EU decisions. In particular, directives on minimum standards for appliances, the rules on the development of energy markets and the role of renewables and energy efficiency, and extending and upgrading energy labels. None of these can be undertaken by the individual member states, so in a real sense, the EU is responsible for the basic momentum of greenhouse gas reductions. Since the signing of the Kyoto Protocol in 1996, the Commission has failed to provide the necessary leadership in this policy arena. The potential savings by 2010 from more efficient domestic lights and appliances has already declined by nearly 25% (from 2.7 to 2 MtC). In addition, consumption is increasing in several member states, when it should be declining. This should ring alarm-bells with each of us as individuals who are concerned about the risk to future generations, but also because of the resultant policy implications; more will have to be achieved in a shorter time scale at greater expense.

National governments
It is the separate member state governments that undertake to comply with the Kyoto Protocol and accept legally-binding targets. It is these governments that will have to implement rapid policy interventions, in order to redeem the situation, if the other actors are unable to provide the necessary progress. A major improvement in the efficiency of an appliance can be achieved, through negotiations with manufacturers, over a 6-10 year time scale at minimal or nil cost to the consumer, because it is absorbed into future production designs. To achieve the same result in less time risks confrontations with industry as well as higher costs for consumers. The window of opportunity is still open, but only just - 2010 is approaching fast.

A further set of actions that will be required of national governments, particularly if progress is slow, is to achieve carbon savings through the direct promotion of fuel switching. This has previously been a contentious issue in some countries. The situation may be changing, partly because so many utilities are not dual fuel (selling both gas and electricity). On several front, the member states, particularly in their negotiations in the EU, may need to be more proactive and aggressive in developing lower carbon futures.

8.2   FURTHER RESEARCH NEEDED
Priorities for further research to ensure that the Kyoto+ savings are achieved, and to begin to plan for the future savings beyond that, are outlined below.

This study has re-confirmed the key importance of efficiency improvements to electrical appliances as a means of reducing carbon emissions from the domestic sector. Considerable research is already on going within the EU on electrical efficiency options for many of the major appliances. However, there are still areas requiring further work. For example, in the UK, research on national electrical efficiency options for hot water cylinders and kettles is required. Research is also required on the design of appliances that prompt awareness about excessive or unnecessary consumption, and on the response of householders to these appliances.

A key sector of increasing energy demand is consumer electronics. There are many issues including power demand, levels of service and the platform chosen, which will determine eventual energy consumption by this sector. This is an area in which policy makers need to anticipate new developments and to react quickly. Thought is required as to how policy making, which can be quite slow (as illustrated in Chapter 5), can accelerate when necessary to prevent industry decisions which will entail additional, unnecessary energy use.

Use of corporate average efficiency schemes as a policy instrument should be further investigated. This was suggested for both boilers and light bulbs. Lighting is one of the two sectors with the greatest potential for savings, and further effective policy needs to be developed on an EU level, rather than relying heavily on national subsidy schemes to increase the uptake of CFLs. The potential role of a Corporate Average Bulb Efficiency target should be developed further. In addition, the use of this type of policy instrument for production of gas and electrical appliances should be considered.

The impact of increasing numbers of one-person households has been highlighted. More work is needed to establish the opportunities for policy intervention to facilitate energy savings by this section of the population.

Chapter 7 highlighted the difficulties of obtaining good energy consumption data by end use for many EU countries. A European reference data set is required.

Work on the Sustainability Scenario concluded that even with comprehensive packages of policy instruments to enable changes in behaviour, to get domestic emissions on the path to sustainability considerable further effort to increase use of renewable energy would be required. There are considerable opportunities at the household level, as well as the more familiar supply side options. Policy on these should be developed in tandem with efficiency opportunities, for example, solar hot water systems will save additional carbon when used with a hot-fill or heat-fed washing machine. Household PV systems should be installed with packages of super-efficient lighting and appliances.

The Sustainability Scenario also highlighted another key theme of this report – which is the importance of informing and motivating all actors (consumers, retailers, manufacturers, installers and others) if considerable carbon savings are to be made. The role of new and innovative methods of information provision has also been highlighted. More effort should be made in identifying effective means of communication and motivation, with particular attention being paid to existing successful initiatives in different member states.

8.3   CONCLUDING REMARKS

Around 3.7 MtC could be saved by 2010 in the UK, Netherlands and Portugal through policies to increase the efficiency of gas and electricity use, and to encourage fuel switching to natural gas in lighting, appliances and water heating. These savings would be achieved without any drop in the level of service provided to consumers and are delivered through the sale of more energy efficient LAWH and more gas fired appliances. The policies depend upon a strategic approach to carbon dioxide emissions in this sector that is strongly supported both in the member states and in the European Commission. Many new and innovative policy instruments have been identified to make these savings, both for energy efficiency and fuel switching, thus offering policy makers a variety of pathways to a lower carbon future.

REFERENCES

Adato Energia Oy (1999) Juhani Kalevi, Adato Energia Oy [owned by the Finnish Electricity Association, the Finnish Energy Industries Federation and the Finnish District Heat Association], personal communication, September 1999, Helsinki, Finland

Appliance (1997) *Appliance*, November

Bach, P. (1999) *Energy savings – use of efficient technology and change in consumer behaviour*, in Proceedings of European Council for an Energy Efficient Economy, Summer Study. ADEME Editions, Paris

BAK (1997) *EnergieNed/Basisonderzoek Aardgasverbruik Kleinverbruikers*. RJ Weegink, Aprii 1998, Arnhem, NL

Bertoldi, P., Bowie, R. and Hagen, L. (1998) *The Use of Negotiated Agreements to Improve Efficiency of End-Use Appliances: First Results from the European Experience*. Proceedings from the 1998 ACEEE Summer Study on Energy Efficient Buildings. Energy Efficiency in a Competitive Environment

BEK (1996) *EnergieNed/Basisonderzoek Elektriciteitsverbruik Kleinverbruikers* 1996. RJ Weegink, June 1997, Arnhem, NL

BEK (1995) *Basisonderzoek Elektriciteitsverbruik Kleinverbruikers* 1995. EnergieNed, Arnhem, NL

BFE (1999) Beroepsfederatie van de Producenten en Verdelers van Elektriciteit in Belgie (Federation of Electricity Generators and Distributors in Belgium), personal communication, 1999.

BFE (1998) *Annuaire Statistique 1997*. Produced by the Fédération Professionelle des Producteurs et Distributeurs d'Électricité de Belgique, Brussels.

BG (1998) *British Gas plc, 1997 Annual Report*. Information web published at www.bgplc.com/databook/stats, accessed 27/4/98.

BGE (1999) Bord Gáis Éireann, information web published at http://www.bge.ie/.

Boardman, B., Bullock, S. and McLaren, D. (1999) *Equity and the environment, guidelines for green and socially just government*. Catalyst pamphlet 5. ISBN 0 9533224 4 0

Boardman, B. (1991) *Fuel Poverty*. Belhaven Press, London

BRE (1998) *Domestic Energy Fact File*. L.D. Shorrock and G.A.Walters, Building Research Establishment, Watford, UK, March 1998

British Gas (1998) *British Gas Annual Review*, at: http://www.bgplc.com

BSRIA (1995) *UK market for water heating*. Report 11934/2, June

CEG (1998) Évolution des Taux de Pénétration des Principaux Appareils Électroménagers. Data supplied by BFE by personal communication 1999.

CEREN (1998) *Suivi du Parc et des Consommations*. Data supplied by ADEME, March 1999

CSO (1998) Personal communication, Central Statistics Office, Cork, Ireland.

Dansk Naturgas (1999) Personal communication, Dansk Olie Og Naturgas A/S (DONG), January 1999. DONG is the association of Danish natural gas suppliers.

DEA (1999) *Energy in Denmark 1998: Development, Policies and Results.* Web published at http://www.ens.dk/pub/energy98/index.htm

DEA (1998) *Energi 1997.* Data sent by Danish Energy Agency, personal communication 1998

DEA (1995) *Denmark's Energy Futures.* Published by the Danish Energy Agency and the Ministry of Environment and Energy, Copenhagen, 1995 (English version published 1996).

DECADE (1997a) *Transforming the UK Cold Market.* Energy and Environment Programme, Environmental Change Unit, University of Oxford, UK

DECADE (1997b) *2MtC – 2 million tonnes of carbon.* Energy and Environment Programme, Environmental Change Unit, University of Oxford, UK

DEF (1999) Personal communication, Dansk Elvaerkers Forening (DEF), January 1999. DEF is the association of Danish electric utilities.

DELight (1997) *DELight - Domestic Efficient Lighting.* Energy and Environment Programme. Environmental Change Unit, University of Oxford

DESWH (1998) *Analysis of energy efficiency of domestic electric storage water heaters.* Study for the Directorate General for Energy (DGXVII) of the Commission of the European Communities, Final Report

DETR (1999c) *English House Condition Survey 1996.* Information web published at http://www.housing.detr.gov.uk/research/ehcs96/.

DETR (1998) *Climate change consultation paper* – October

DETR (1997) *Press Release 203.* Environment ministerial speech at WWF conference, 4 June 1997, London, UK

Dörfler, H. and Riess, R. (1995) *Statistiche Nachrichten* (6)/1995, Austria

Doxa S.p.A. (1998) Data supplied by Politecnico di Milano, personal communication, 1998.

DTI (1998) *Transforming the Market.* Department of Trade and Industry Energy Report

DTI (1997) *Energy Consumption in the United Kingdom,* Energy Paper 66, December 1997 Department of Trade and Industry (DTI), HMSO, London, UK

DTI (1995) *Energy Projections for the UK,* Energy Paper 65. Department of Trade and Industry (DTI), HMSO, London, UK

DUKES (1999) *Digest of UK Energy Statistics.* Department of Trade and Industry (DTI), HMSO, London, UK

DUKES (1998) *Digest of UK Energy Statistics,* Department of Trade and Industry (DTI), HMSO, London, UK

EHCS (1996) *English House Condition Survey 1991, Energy Report.* Department of the Environment, HMSO, London, UK

Ecofys (2000) *District Heating in the Netherlands*. E4068/MaB

Ecofys (1998) Personal communication, 1998

EdF (1999) Electricité de France. *Company information*, web published at:
http://www.edf.fr/html/en/presentation/index.html

Eggar, C. and Dell, G. (1999) *The regional energy plan of Upper Austria: 12% CO$_2$ reduction in 4 years*, in Proceedings of European Council for an Energy-Efficient Economy, Summer Study 1999. ADEME Editions, Paris

ENDS (1999) *ENDS*, September

ENEA (1999) Ente per le Nuove Tecnologie, *l'Energia e l'Ambiente* personal communication (Dr. Giovanni Perella), April 1999

EnergieNed (1998) *Energiedistributie in Nederland 1997*. EnergieNed (the association of Dutch energy distribution companies), Arnhem, the Netherlands

ESB (1999) Information web published at http://www2.esb.ie/htm/home/index.htm. Electricity Supply Board, Dublin, Ireland.

ESIF (1995) *Sun in action, the solar thermal market, a strategic plan for action in Europe*, European Solar Industry Federation, Commission of the European Communities, DG XVII, Contract No 4.1030/E/94-003

ESource (1996) *Technology Atlas Series V: Residential Appliances*. E Source, Inc. (Rocky Mountain Institute Research Associates), Boulder, Colorado, USA

EST (1998) *Energy efficiency standards of performance* 1994-1998, p16. Energy Savings Trust

EST (1999) *Review 1998/99 and workplan 1999/2000*. Energy Saving Trust, London

Eurogas (1998) Eurogas Key Figures 1997/8. *In: Natural Gas in Western Europe – 1998 publication of gas statistics and prospects*. Information web published at www.eurogas.org. Eurogas, Brussels, Belgium.

Euromonitor (1996) *European Marketing Forecasts 1996*. London, UK

European Commission, DG XI (1996) COM (96) 561

European Commission, DG XI (1999) COM (99) 230 19 May 1999. *Preparing for Implementation of the Kyoto Protocol*

European Commission (1999a) *Energy in Europe 1998 – Annual Energy Review*. Office for Official Publications of the European Communities, Luxembourg.

European Commission, DG XVII (1998) COM (98) 246. *Energy Efficiency in the European Community – Towards a Strategy for the Rational Use of Energy*

European Environment Agency (1999) *Environment in the European Union at the Turn of the Century*, Office for Official Publications of the European Communities, Luxembourg

European Environment Agency (1995) *Europe's Environment: The Dobris Assessment*. Stanners D. and Bourdeau P (eds). Office for Official Publications of the European Communities, Luxembourg

Eurostat (1998) *Social Portrait of Europe*. Statistical Office of the European Communities, Luxembourg. ISBN 92-827-9093-2, printed September 1998

EVA (1998) *Analysis of Energy Efficiency of Domestic Electric Storage Water Heaters*. Final Report, SAVE Contract N° 4.1031/E/95-013

EVA (1998a) Data from the Odyssee Database, 1997; supplied by EVA, personal communication, 1998.

Evans, R.D., and H.P.J. Herring (1989) *Energy use and energy efficiency in the UK domestic sector up to the year 2010*. Department of Energy, HMSO, London

FIGAS (1997) *Statistical Yearbook of the Belgian Federation of Gas Industries*. Information web published at http://web.arcadis.be/eurogasfigas/.

Finergy/Sener (1998) *Electricity in Finland*. Brochure produced by the Finnish Energy Industries Federation (Finergy) and the Finnish Electricity Association (Sener), Finland.

Fyrogenis (1999) Personal communication, Athens, August 1999.

GasTec (1996) *Framework for a European method to determine the energy consumption for domestic hot water production*. Final Report of SAVE Contract No. 4.1031/Z/95-052. The Netherlands, June

GEA (1995b) *Washing machines, dishwashers and dryers: Final report*. Group for Efficient Appliances, Working Group - European Energy Network (E^{n}R). Danish Energy Agency, Denmark

GdF (1999) Gaz de France. Company information, web published at: http://www.gazdefrance.com/anglais/index.htm

Global Commons Institute (1998) http://www.gn.apc.org/gci

Green, J., Darby, S., Maby, C., and Boardman, B. (1998) *Advice into action – an evaluation of the effectiveness of energy advice to low-income households*. Eaga Charitable Trusts, Keswick, UK.

Hinnells, M.J. and McMahon, J. (1997) *Stakeholders and market transformation: an integrated analysis of costs and benefits*. Proceedings of the European Council for an Energy Efficient Economy summer study in energy efficiency, June 1997, Danish Energy Agency, Copenhagen, Denmark

IEA (1998) *Natural Gas Distribution – Focus on Western Europe*. International Energy Agency, December

IEA (1996) *Energy Policies of IEA Countries – Spain – 1996 Review*. International Energy Agency, June

IEA/OECD (1998b) *Energy Balances of OECD Countries, 1995-1996*. IEA Statistics, OECD, Paris, France

IEC (1996) *Statistical report on energy use in Irish households in 1995*. Irish Energy Centre, Dublin.

IER (1998) *Evaluation and Comparison of Utilities and Governmental DSM Programmes for the Promotion of Condensing Boilers*. University of Stuttgart. Save contract: XVII 4.103\2\96-136

IPCC (1995) *Climate Change 1995, The Science of Climate Change*. Contribution of IPCC Working Group I to the Second Assessment Report of the Intergovernmental Panel on Climate Change, Cambridge University Press, UK

ISR (1999) Catarina Nunes, personal communication 1999

ISR (1998) Catarina Nunes, personal communication, 1998

ISTAT (1998) *Italy in Figures,* Instituto Nazionale di Statistica, Rome, Italy

Kasanen, P (1999) *EU domestic ovens, SAVE study.* TTS, Finland

Key Statistics (1991) *1991 Census. Key Statistics for Urban and Rural Areas, Great Britain,* p278. Office for National Statistics

Konsumenverket (1998) Data supplied by Arthur Horowitz, Konsumentverket, for the SAVE Ovens Study 1998.

Kouloumoundras, S. (1999) Personal communication from Spiros Kouloumoundras, Copelouzos Group of Companies (joint stakeholder in the Greek gas supplier Prometheus Gas S.A., along with the Russian natural gas export company VEP GazExport). August 1999.

LEEP (1996) *Securing the Savings: a report on the first two years of the Billsavers project.* Lothian and Edinburgh Environmental Partnership, Edinburgh, UK.

Maakaasuyhdistys (1999) Finnish Natural Gas Association, personal communication, November 1999.

Mabro, R. and Wybrew-Bond, I. (eds) (1999) *Gas to Europe: The Strategies of Four Major Suppliers.* Published by Oxford University Press for the Oxford Institute for Energy Studies, June

McLaren, D., S. Bullock and N. Yousuf (1998) *Tomorrow's World: Britain's Share in a Sustainable Future*, Earthscan, London

Minez (1997) *Renewable Energy, Advancing Power.* Action Programme 1997 - 2000 of the Netherlands Ministry for Economic Affairs. Available from http://info.minez.nl/ezenglish/

Noorman, K.J., and T.S. Uiterkamp (eds) (1998) *Green Households? Domestic Consumers, Environment and Sustainability.* Earthscan, London

Nørgård, J (1996) *Technical energy savings versus changes in human behaviour*, in Proceedings of SAVE working conference on influencing energy-related behaviour in Europe, Amsterdam, 30 Nov-1 Dec. 1995

NOVEM (1999) *EU labelling and information systems: Installed Appliances Workshop*, March 4-5, Utrecht, Netherlands

NSSG (1999) National Statistical Service of Greece, Electricity consumption information sent by personal communication, 1999.

NUTEK (1995) *Small machines for small households.* Swedish National Board for Industrial and Technical Development

OECD (1999) *National Climate Policies and the Kyoto Protocol.* OECD

Office for National Statistics (1998) *Family Spending, a report on the 1997-98 Family Expenditure Survey.* HMSO, London, UK

OFGEM (1999) *Energy efficiency.* A Consultation Document. London

ONS (1998) *Social Trends 28, 1998 edition.* Office for National Statistics. Stationery Office, London, UK

Palmer, J. (1997) *How many people does it take to change a light bulb?* in Proceedings of the European Council for an Energy Efficient Economy, Summer Study, Danish Energy Agency

PPC (1999) Public Power Corporation, personal communication, July 1999, Athens, Greece.

Prognos (1995) *Die Energiemärkte Deutschlands im Zusammenwachsenden Europa – Perspektiven bis 2020*. Auftrag des Bundesministeriums für Wirtschaft, Basel, Switzerland.

Ruhrgas (1999) *Natural Gas in Europe*. Published by Ruhrgas Economics and Energy Industry Department.

Sachs, W., R. Loske and M. Linz (1998) *Greening the North: A post-industrial blueprint for ecology and equity*, Zed Books, London

Sadalla, E.K. and Krull, J.L. (1995) Self-presentational barriers to resource conservation. *Environment and Behaviour*, Vol. 27, No.3, 328-353

SAP (1998) The Government's Standard Assessment Procedure for Energy Rating of Dwellings. DETR. BRECSU, BRE

Sedigas (1998a) *La Industria del Gas en España; 1997 Avance Estadistico*. Sedigas Barcelona, Spain.

Southerton, D. and Shove, L. (1999) *'Consumption, Everyday Life and Sustainability'*, ESF TERM Programme, Lancaster University, United Kingdom, March 1998

SNAM (1999) Personal communication, October 1999.

Statistics Finland (1998) *Energy Consumption in Households 1995*, National Report for the Eurostat project "Household Energy Consumption". January 1998.

Stern, J.P. (1998) *Competition and Liberalization in European Gas Markets – A Diversity of Models*. Energy and Environmental Programme, the Royal Institute of International Affairs, London.

Svenska Gasföreningen (1999) Personal communication, Göran Engström, Swedish Gas Association, January 1999.

Tanabe, K (2000) *New integrated metering systems for household electricity, gas and water costs*. The Energy Conservation Centre, Japan.

TTS (1999) Työtehoseura (TTS Work Efficiency Institute), personal communication, March 1999

VDEW (1996) *VDEW-Haushaltskundenbefrafung* 1996, Frankfurt, Germany.

Vringer, K., Potting, J., and K. Blok (1995) *A reduction in the indirect energy requirement of households*. In: Proceedings of the Energy Efficiency Challenge for Europe, 1995 Summer Study. European Council for an Energy-Efficient Economy

Waide, P. (1999) *Monitoring of energy efficiency trends of European domestic refrigeration appliances*. Final report. SAVE contract number XVII/4.1031/D/97-021, PW Consulting, UK.

Waide, P. and Herring, H. (1993) *Mandatory energy efficiency standards for domestic refrigeration units in the European Community: analysis of the draft EC Directive and alternative proposals for a standard*. Greenpeace International, London, UK

Weber, C. and A. Perrels (2000, forthcoming) Modelling lifestyle effects on energy demand and related emissions. *Energy Policy*, Universitat Stuttgart and TNO-Inro, Stuttgart and Delft

White Knight (undated) *Watch your costs tumble*, sales brochure for tumble dryers

Wilhite, H. and Lutzenhiser, L. (1997) *Social loading and sustainable consumption.* Proceedings of the 1997 ECEEE conference, Panel 4, ID 27

Wilhite, H. and R. Ling (1995) Measured energy savings from a more informative energy bill. *Energy and buildings* 22, pp145-155

Winkler, R.A. and Winett, R. (1982) Behavioural interventions in resource management: a systems approach based on behavioural economics. *American Psychologist,* Vol. 37, 421-435

Winward, J., Schiellerup, P., Boardman B.. (1998) *Cool Labels. The first three years of the European Energy Label.* Environmental Change Unit, University of Oxford.

Wolf, W. and Kronsteiner, C. (1995) Ausstattung der Haushalter: Zeitvergleich nach sozialer Stellung, Gemeindetyp und Bündesländern. *Statistiche Nachrichten* (1)/1995, p22-32.

Young, B. (2000) *Boilers for Domestic Space Heating and Hot Water in the United Kingdom.* A Sector Review Paper on Projected Energy Consumption for the Department of the Environment, Transport and the Regions

GLOSSARY

Aggregated purchase/ Energy+ - the aim of aggregated purchase is to increase the market share of the most efficient appliances on the market. By gathering together buyers (whether purchasers of the technology or retailers) considerable purchasing power can be exerted on manufacturers to provide efficient appliances at a cheaper price. A large guaranteed market in turn allows manufacturers to access economies of scale. Energy+ is the name of the current EU aggregated purchase pilot project for fridge-freezers.

Boiler – a gas- or liquid-fuelled appliance designed to provide hot water for space heating. It may (but need not) be designed to provide domestic hot water as well.

BP (Behavioural potential) - an estimate of how much energy could be saved by changes in behaviour relative to projected consumption in the Reference Case. The behavioural changes identified for the BP must meet three criteria - they must be actions that: do not result in a loss of service to the consumer; can be carried out immediately by the consumer; have zero cost. The BP does not therefore identify all of the potential energy savings through behaviour. The proviso that there should be no loss of service fits with the philosophy underlying ETP.

Business As Usual (BAU) scenario - see reference case.

Butane – Hydrocarbon (C_4H_{10}), gaseous at normal temperature, but generally stored and transported as a liquid. Used as a component in Motor Spirit to improve combustion, and for cooking and heating (see LPG).

Carbon dioxide (CO_2) - a major greenhouse gas and the main gas produced when fossil fuels are burnt. One molecule contains one atom of carbon and two atoms of oxygen, with the relative molecular masses of 12:16:16. Carbon dioxide can be weighed on the basis of either the carbon content (12) or the whole molecule (44). In this report the weight is based on carbon content and given as MtC (million tonnes of carbon). (To convert carbon to CO_2, multiply by 44/12).

CEC (European Commission) - the civil service of the European Community. Directorate General XVII (Energy) is responsible for the SAVE programme, of which the Cadence project is a part.

Central heating system - a heating system with a distribution system sufficient to provide heat in at least one room in addition to the room or space containing the boiler. In this report, the definition also includes electric storage heaters that run on off-peak electricity and programmable gas convector heaters.

CFCs – chlorofluorocarbons (CFCs) are a group of compounds which were commonly used as refrigerants in domestic cold appliances. After being identified as a prime contributor to the depletion of the ozone layer and the subsequent agreement of the Montreal Protocol, their use has been phased out in cold appliances.

CFLs (compact fluorescent lamps) - these low energy bulbs can replace ordinary incandescents.

Cold appliances - see Appendix A (also for **Wet, Cooking** and **Miscellaneous appliances**).

Consumer electronics – see Appendix A.

Combi boiler - an instantaneous gas boiler that heats water for space and hot water system direct from the water mains. Therefore there is no need for either a hot or cold water storage tank. Combi boilers can also be condensing.

Condensing boilers – the most efficient available. Both the latent and sensible heat produced is recovered (conventional boilers do not recover latent heat) by cooling flue gas to below 100°C. When the condensing boiler is operating at maximum efficiency, flue gas temperatures of around 54°C are achieved and the boiler operates in its condensing mode - the steam in the flue gas gives up its latent heat to the boiler and condenses out. If the flue gases are above 54°C the condensing boiler does not operate in its condensing mode but is still a highly efficient non-condensing boiler. Condensing boilers produce a plume of water vapour, and thus should not be situated near a door or window or very close to a neighbour's property. For this reason and the need to drain condensate mean that condensing boilers are not appropriate for all uses.

CORGI – the Council for Registered Gas Installers (UK). Responsible to the Health and Safety Executive for maintenance of a register of competent installers, and for the promotion of both industrial and public gas safety. Since 1991, all gas installation businesses have had to be CORGI registered.

Demand side management (DSM) - policies to reduce the demand for electricity, either in a general sense or, often, as a specific policy of an electricity utility.

DESHW Study – the DESHW (domestic electric stored hot water) study analysed design options which improve insulation, and therefore reduce the rate of heat loss. 41% of standing losses could be eliminated by 2020 if all EU water heaters moved to the best currently available on the market.

EA (Electricity Association) - UK organisation representing the 19 electricity companies involved in generation, transmission and distribution of electricity in the UK, and known as the Electricity Council prior to electricity privatisation in 1991.

Ecolabel - a label assessed on the basis of a complete life cycle analysis. Criteria allow only the best 10 or 20% of products on the market to qualify, but the manufacturer has to pay a licence fee to use the Ecolabel logo.

EESOP - (Energy Efficiency Standards of Performance) – in the UK Public Electricity Supply companies were required by the Electricity Regulator to spend the equivalent of £1 (1.5 Euro) per customer per year, during the period 1994-98, on the more efficient use of electricity. This amounted to a total investment of £100 million (150m Euro), 25% of which was originally targeted at electrical appliances in the domestic sector. However, in practice less has been spent since insufficient schemes were forthcoming. Most of the investment to date has been on lighting. From April 200, the amount is increased to £1.20 (1.8 Euro)

Efficiency index – The (energy) efficiency index is a ratio calculated by dividing the annual energy consumption of an appliance by its standard energy consumption. The standard annual energy consumption is calculated in accordance with EU Directive 94/2/EC and takes into account the appliance's adjusted volume, whether or not it is frost-free, and correction factors based on appliances available on the EU market. The efficiency index can also be expressed as a percentage (i.e., the ratio multiplied by 100).

Energy efficiency - energy consumed by an operation or series of operations per unit capacity (e.g., kWh/kg) and per unit of performance (e.g., at 60°C).

ESCO – An ESCO, or Energy Service Company, can be broadly defined as a company supplying energy and providing measures to encourage its efficient use. Few domestic sector examples exist. The ESCO invests capital in the house to reduce consumption per unit of service and recoups the cost through higher energy costs.

ETP (Economic and technical potential) - ETP is technically feasible *and* cost-effective to the consumer. *Cost effective* means it is the minimum life cycle cost (See Life Cycle Cost). *Feasible* means it is proven technology. Other assumptions are average usage patterns, current EU prices for electricity, water and equipment, average market mark-ups and an 8% discount rate. If energy or equipment prices change significantly, or if new technologies become available, then the ETP may change. It does not include any reduction in consumption from changes in behaviour, and so does not represent the technical limit or the lowest limit on consumption.

ETP2005 - a scenario in which all appliances are assumed to reach ETP efficiency level by 2005.

EU (European Union) - The EU was established by the Maastricht treaty and comprises the European Community (Austria, Belgium, Denmark, Finland, France, Germany, Greece, Ireland, Italy, Luxembourg, the Netherlands, Portugal, Spain, Sweden and the United Kingdom), a Foreign Defence and Security Co-operation Mechanism and a Home Affairs and Justice Co-operation Mechanism.

Euro - The exchange rate for the Netherlands is fixed at 1 Euro = 2.2037 NLG, for Portugal 1 Euro = 200.482 PTE. The UK has a floating exchange rate with the Euro, for this report 1 Euro = £0.667.

European Commission - see CEC.

Frost-free - Frost builds up in a freezer or fridge-freezer as the air inside cools and contracts, sucking in warm humid air, which then freezes. In a 'frost-free' appliance, air is driven by fan through a duct and cooled outside the cabinet insulation, so that between cycles the evaporator plate rises above freezing and any ice melts. Fans, heaters and the loss of efficiency from cooling outside the insulation all result in additional consumption which, for a fridge-freezer in the UK, can be up to an extra 50%.

GB (Great Britain) - the three mainland countries of England, Wales and Scotland, i.e., not including Northern Ireland.

HEES (Home Energy Efficiency Scheme) – a UK government-funded scheme to provide basic home energy efficiency improvements, such as loft insulation, draught proofing and improved boilers for householders on means-tested benefit.

Household - a group of people (who may or may not be related) living, or staying temporarily, at the same address, who have a regular arrangement to share at least one meal daily *or* share common housekeeping. This is the definition used in all official UK Government publications.

IEA (International Energy Agency) - independent organisation of 24 Member countries, established within the framework of OECD to carry out a comprehensive and co-operative development programme for sustainable international energy trade.

Instantaneous combination boiler – a combination boiler without an internal hot water store, or with an internal hot water store of capacity not exceeding 15 litres.

Integrated resource planning (IRP) – is when a 'planning entity', for example a utility, evaluates the conservation and efficiency resource on an equal footing with the expansion of productive capacity on the supply side in the process of planning how to best meet future demand.

kWh (kilowatt-hour) - measure of electrical energy consumed; 1 kWh is equal to 1000 watts used for 1 hour.

Life cycle cost - The cost of the appliance to the consumer over the lifetime of the appliance (i.e., running costs as well as purchase price). Design changes in favour of efficiency may increase purchase price yet make such large savings in running costs that, over the life of the appliance, they reduce the total life cycle cost. Other more expensive design options may increase life cycle cost. A case could be made for any combination of options which did not increase the life cycle cost above its current level, but resulted in the minimum level of emissions (Figure A.1). However, ETP in this report is based on minimum life cycle cost.

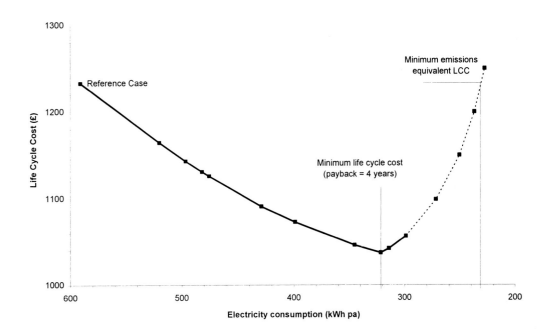

Figure A. 1 Electricity consumption and life cycle cost for fridge-freezers

Life time (of an appliance) - the time taken for half the number of appliances to leave the stock (also known as life span). In the DECADE model, for example, this is taken to be 13 years for refrigerators, 18 years for fridge-freezers and 14.5 years for a tumble dryer.

Liquefied Petroleum Gas (LPG) – gas usually propane or butane, derived from oil and under pressure so that it is in liquid form. Often used to power cooking stoves or water heaters.

Minimum standards - legislation to enforce a minimum level of energy efficiency, a maximum level of energy consumption or the presence or absence of a particular technology.

NFFO – the Non Fossil Fuel Obligation is a requirement on English and Welsh regional electricity companies to purchase renewable electricity. This is funded through a levy on electricity prices and is a key part of UK government policy on increasing the use of renewables.

Ownership - the total number of appliances divided by the number of households owning at least one of that appliance, e.g., TV ownership in 1996 was 1.7 sets per household.

Propane – hydrocarbon containing three carbon atoms (C_3H_8), gaseous at normal temperature, but generally stored and transported under pressure as a liquid (see LPG).

Photovoltaics (PV) – the direct conversion of solar radiation into electricity by the interaction of light with the electrons in a semiconductor device or cell.

Reference Case (RC) - a projection of usage and ownership and the underlying rate of technical change determined from historical data where available. The only policy intervention included is that which has been implemented or is close to implementation in the EU member states. This is often known as the Business as Usual scenario.

Regular boiler – a boiler which does not have the capacity to provide domestic hot water directly (i.e. not a combination boiler). It may nevertheless provide domestic hot water indirectly via a separate hot water storage cylinder.

Sales-weighted data – market data which is weighted (for efficiency, energy consumption etc.) according to sales of each model. Sales-weighted data are essential for analysing the effects of policy instruments such as labels, rebates and technology procurement, which might increase the market share of efficient models.

SOP - see EESOP.

Specific energy consumption - energy consumed per unit of service, given a minimum standard of performance (e.g., kWh/litre of cold space at a specified temperature).

Stock of appliances - all the appliances owned by households.

Standby - the mode when an appliance is in a waiting state, a secondary or non-essential state, or is not performing any useful service. It is common in TVs, receiver-decoders, clock-radios, microwaves, computers and other such electronic devices, but can be extended to include appliances with unnecessary or too high transformer power losses.

Takeback – where improved efficiency is taken in the form of increased level of service, rather than reduced energy consumption.

Test procedure - energy used according to defined conditions and international standards. A standardised test procedure is essential for comparing models on a similar basis, but difficult to translate into actual consumption. For instance, the test procedure for cold appliances (EN 153) assumes a warm ambient temperature (25°C) to compensate for no door openings.

UK (United Kingdom) - Great Britain plus Northern Ireland.

Usage patterns - the way in which an appliance is actually used in the home. This can include frequency of use (e.g., for washing machines, the number of washes per annum) and manner of use (eg the proportion of washes at different temperatures).

Watt (W) - SI unit of active electric power; the rate at which electric energy is used.

Wet appliances - see Appendix A.

UNITS OF MEASUREMENT

1 kWh   = 3.6 MJ

POWERS OF TEN

10^3 = kilo (K)
10^6 = mega (M)
10^9 = giga (G)
10^{12} = tera (T)

APPENDIX A: LIST OF APPLIANCES

The lights and appliances included in the DECADE model are as listed below.

COLD APPLIANCES

Chest freezers
Fridge-freezers: two door combination refrigerators
Refrigerators: one door refrigerators with or without frozen compartment
Upright freezers

CONSUMER ELECTRONICS

Answering machine
Cable control boxes for TVs, analogue and digital
Cassette players
Clock
Clock radios
Computer printers
Cordless telephones, analogue and digital
Digital receiver decoders
Fax machines
Hi-fi
Mobile telephone chargers
Other office equipment: slide projectors, electric typewriters etc
Personal computers
Satellite control boxes for TVs, analogue and digital
Televisions
VCRs (video cassette recorders)

COOKING APPLIANCES

Major appliances
Electric kettles: includes all types of electric kettle
Hobs, gas and electric
Microwaves: includes combination microwave/grill/convection ovens
Oven including grills, gas and electric

Minor appliances
Cooker hoods
Coffee makers
Deep fat fryers
Food preparation appliances: mixers, blenders, processors, whisks etc
Electric frying pans
Sandwich toasters
Slow cookers
Toasters

LIGHTING

CFL (compact fluorescent light bulb)
Fluorescent strip
Halogen bulbs

Incandescent bulbs: 100W, 60W and 40W

MISCELLANEOUS APPLIANCES

Central heating pumps
DIY equipment: drills, torches, battery chargers etc
Electric blankets
Electric towel rails
Garden equipment: lawn mowers, strimmers, hedge trimmers etc
Hair care equipment: hair dryers, curling tongs etc
Home care equipment: sewing machines, floor polishers etc
Irons
Personal care appliances: electric toothbrushes, electric razors etc
Vacuum cleaners

WATER HEATING

Domestic electric stored water heating (DESWH)
Electric instantaneous water heaters (E-INST)
Electric showers
Natural gas instantaneous water heaters (G-INST)
Natural gas combined space and water heating (CSWH)
LPG instantaneous water heaters (Portugal only) (LPG-INST)

WET APPLIANCES

Dishwashers: all dishwashers
Tumble dryers: all types of dryers including the drying cycle of washer-dryers, gas and electric
Washing machines: any automatic washing machine including the washing cycle of washer-dryers

APPENDIX B : PROFILES OF CONTRIBUTORS

ECI

DR NICK BANKS after completing a doctorate entitled "Cultural Values and the Adoption of Energy Efficient Technologies" at the Environmental Change Institute, Nick joined the Energy and Environment team. At present he is working on a review of vehicle efficiency labelling schemes for the DETR and is responsible for the social dimensions of the CADENCE project. Nick also has responsibilities for the Consumer Electronics sector and is Webmaster of the ECI.

DR BRENDA BOARDMAN, MBE was PowerGen Fellow in Energy Efficiency at St Hilda's College 1991-1999, and is the programme leader for the Energy and Environment Programme. She specialises in the efficient use of energy in the UK domestic sector, in particular the policy implications and problems faced by low-income households. She is acknowledged as the leading UK researcher on fuel poverty, and is responsible for the concept of affordable warmth. She has published widely and is regularly called upon for expert contributions to conferences, specialist workshops and the UK media. In addition to managing the DECADE project, she has overall responsibility for the Programme's research for the European Commission, Department of the Environment and on rural transport. She was recently awarded an MBE in recognition of her work.

TINA FAWCETT contributes towards the analysis of technology and policy options for reducing carbon emissions. Prior to joining ECI in November 1996, she gained a MSc in Environmental Technology from Imperial College, London and worked for a number of years in waste management, most recently for the Environment Agency.

HARRIET GRIFFIN assists in analysing appliance use data and with research into the socio-economic determinants of household electricity consumption. Before joining the ECI in March 1997 she worked for the Natural History Museum and the Agriculture Development Advisory Service and gained a M.Phil. in Crop Pollination Ecology from the University of St. Andrews.

DR KEVIN LANE is responsible for developing the DECADE model, and applying it to policy analyses for various EU working groups. With a first degree in digital systems and microprocessor engineering, his doctoral research was on the development and application of non-stationary time series analysis techniques to climatological data. He was awarded jointly the World Meteorological Organisation's 1996 Norbert Gerbier Prize. His final project before joining the ECI was the development of the Derwent Water Resources Model (a computer based management model) for the National Rivers Authority.

JUDITH LIPP joined ECI in 1999, after completing the MSc in Environmental Change and Management at the ECI the previous year. Prior to coming to England she worked on Waste Management in Germany and completed an honours degree in Economics at Saint Mary's University in Halifax, Canada. She contributes to the modelling work of the Energy and Environment Programme and aims to become the team's water heating expert.

PERNILLE SCHIELLERUP joined the ECI in 1996. Research interests include EU energy policy and its implementation. Before joining the ECI, she gained a first in Geography and Combined Studies at Oxford Brookes University, and completed the MSc in Environmental Change and Management at the ECI.

DR. RIKI THERIVEL is a research scientist at the Environmental Change Institute, and a visiting professor at Oxford Brookes University's School of Planning. Before joining the ECI she worked for two years for CAG Consultants on issues related to sustainability and land use planning. Her speciality is environmental impact assessment and strategic environmental assessment.

ECOFYS

PROFESSOR KORNELIS BLOK is Scientific Director of Ecofys and professor at the Department of Science, Technology and Society of the University of Utrecht. He has extended research and consultancy experience in the fields of energy efficiency, clean energy production and climate change. He was involved in the research on implementation of energy efficiency options and the design of energy R&D programmes. His research on burden differentiation played an instrumental role in reaching the 1997 agreement on burden sharing within the European Union.

MARGREET VAN BRUMMELEN (MSc) is a consultant in Ecofys' section Energy- and Environmental Policies Studies and has experience in the fields of renewable energy, energy efficiency improvement and (non-CO2) greenhouse gas emission reduction. She was project manager of the Ecofys part of the Cadence project.

KOEN EISING (MSc) graduated in the Science of Public/ Social Administration with a study of organisational behaviour among the realisation of energy efficient houses. He worked for a few years as policy making official for the municipality of Utrecht in the field of energy efficiency and sustainable building. Since June 1999 he has been project manager for Ecofys in the field of social studies and project development (PV sound barriers, energy projects for municipalities).

DR FRANK ZEGERS is Head of Ecofys' Solar Thermal Energy section and senior consultant on thermal solar energy, renewable energy and energy efficiency in the built environment. He was project manager of the national field test with heat-fed washing machines and laundry dryers in co-operation with 7 utilities, EnergieNed, Novem and Gasunie.

DR EDITH MOLENBBROEK is a consultant in Ecofys' Grid Connected PV section, and has experience in the fields of PV-materials research, and performance monitoring of PV-systems. She was assistant project manager of the field-test and analyzed the performance data of the heat-fed washing machines and laundry dryers.

ISR-University of Coimbra

ANNIBAL T. DE ALMEIDA received his BSc in Electrical Engineering with first class honours from the University of Porto in 1972, and a PhD in Electrical Engineering from the University of London in 1977. He has been with the University of Coimbra, where he is currently a Professor in the Department of Electrical Engineering, since 1977. He was a member of the High Technology Panel of the NATO Scientific and Environmental Affairs Division from 1993 to 1999, and is a consultant on the European Commission 4th and 5th Framework programme. He has co-authored five books on energy efficiency, and more than one hundred papers in international journals, meetings and conferences. He was the Chairman of International Conference "Energy Efficiency Improvements in Electric Motors and Drives", held in Lisbon, 29-31 October, 1996.

CATARINA NUNES received an Electrical Engineering degree from the University of Coimbra. She has been involved in ISR-University of Coimbra as researcher in the area of energy efficiency and renewable energies since 1997. She participated in JOULE III BioCosts - Total Costs and Benefits of Biomass in Selected Regions of the European Union, and has been involved in energy audits and in the evaluation of domestic electric storage water heaters.

JORGE DA SILVA MARIANO graduated in Chemical Engineering from the University Oporto, and is now a Professor at Coimbra Polytechnic Institute, industry consultant, and researcher at ISR-University of Coimbra. He has been recognised as Energy Auditor for all industry sectors, by the Portuguese Energy and Industry Ministry, since 1984. He was a senior researcher in several recent projects including: 'Energy Plan of the Centre Region of Portugal', 'Energy Plan of the city of Coimbra', and 'Biocosts - Externality costs associated with the large scale use of biomass'.